SEEDS OF CHANGE FOR THE AQUARIAN

TRANSFORMA

86 Transformational Kriyas & Meditations

VOLUME TWO
SERVING THE INFINITE
Kundalini Yoga as taught by Yogi Bhajan®

Kundalini Research Institute
Training • Publishing • Research • Resources

© 2010 Kundalini Research Institute
Published by the Kundalini Research Institute
PO Box 1819, Santa Cruz, NM 87567
www.kundaliniresearchinstitute.org
ISBN 978-1-934532-39-3

This publication has received the KRI Seal of Approval. This Seal is given only to products that have been reviewed for accuracy and integrity of the sections containing the 3HO lifestyle and Kundalini Yoga as taught by Yogi Bhajan®.

EDITOR

Sat Purkh Kaur Khalsa

CONSULTING EDITORS

Nirvair Singh Khalsa, Tarn Taran Singh Khalsa, Gurucharan Singh Khalsa, Guru Raj Kaur Khalsa

CONTRIBUTORS

Tarn Taran Singh Khalsa and Sat Purkh Kaur Khalsa

KRI REVIEW

Siri Neel Kaur Khalsa

COVER DESIGN

Ravitej Singh Khalsa

BOOK DESIGN & LAYOUT

Guru Raj Kaur Khalsa

PHOTOGRAPHY

Grasshopper Photo, Grace Hopper, photographer; Ravi Tej Singh Khalsa,
Dev Dharam Kaur, Gurudarshan Kaur Khalsa, and Sadhu Kaur Khalsa
Cover Photo of Yogi Bhajan's Mala: Narayan Singh Khalsa

MODELS

Adesh Kaur, Amrit Singh Khalsa, PhD., Ardas Kaur Khalsa, Bhajan Kaur, Bir Kaur O'Flaherty, Deva Kaur Khalsa, Dyal Singh Khalsa, Guru Prakash Singh Khalsa, Har Pal Singh Khalsa, Hargobind Singh Khalsa, Hari Bhajan Kaur Khalsa, Hari Rai Kaur Khalsa, Japa Kaur Khalsa, Jiwan Joti Kaur Khalsa, Jiwan Mukta Singh, Kirn Kaur Khalsa, Lakhmi Chand Singh Khalsa, Nirinjan Kaur Khalsa, Nirmal Singh Khalsa, Panch Nishan Kaur Khalsa, Sadhu Kaur Khalsa, Sat Atma Kaur Khalsa, Sat Purkh Kaur Khalsa, Siri Chand Singh Khalsa, Siri Dyal Kaur Khalsa, Siri Om Kaur Khalsa, Sopurkh Singh Khalsa, Suraj Kaur, Tej Kaur Gaytan, Vanessa Khalsa

Dedication

Photo by Darshan Kaur Khalsa

To our Teacher, the Master of Kundalini Yoga, Yogi Bhajan,
who sacrificed so much to deliver these teachings,
that we might lead, heal and serve the Aquarian Age
with tranquility, transparency, grace and peace.

As another great teacher once said:
"Be the change you wish to see."
Transform your Self and
Transform your world.

Disclaimer

The diet, exercise and lifestyle suggestions in this book come from ancient yogic traditions. Nothing in this book should be construed as medical advice. Any recipes mentioned herein may contain potent herbs, botanicals and naturally occurring ingredients which have traditionally been used to support the structure and function of the human body. Always check with your personal physician or licensed health care practitioner before making any significant modification in your diet or lifestyle, to insure that the ingredients or lifestyle changes are appropriate for your personal health condition and consistent with any medication you may be taking.

For more information about Kundalini Yoga as taught by Yogi Bhajan® please see www.yogibhajan.org or www.kundaliniresearchinstitute.org.

The Fires of Transformation

"The purpose of Kundalini Yoga is transformation." –Yogi Bhajan

At different points in our lives, all of us go through the proverbial fires of transformation. For some it's a break-up, for others it's the death of a loved one, and still for others it's the loss of a job, or a personal health issue, or struggles with addiction. Whatever the fire may be called, we all have to walk through it in order to get to the other side. This process is called transformation and it is, by nature, purifying. It used to be known as alchemy, that mysterious process in which the gross was transmuted into gold. Today we call it consciousness and like the alchemy of old, our personal transformation requires heat, pressure, and time—the purifying fires of *tapas*, the pressure of a sadh sangat, and the discipline of a practice over time—and a little touch of magic I call grace.

Whether it's the psychic heat we create when we burn our egos up with devotion or the physical heat we create when we do Breath of Fire for 31 minutes, each action, though radically different in its outward form, creates *tapas*—or heat—and purifies us, transforms us. Carbon doesn't become a diamond without the tremendous pressure of gravity. As Kundalini Yogis, our gravity is our lifestyle, the practices of this path. It's not easy going out into the world wearing white or covering our head. It isn't easy to change everything—what we eat, what we drink, what time we go to bed—but that is what's required. So, we live in a community of like-minded practitioners—sadh sangat—so that our new way of life is supported and so it's just that much more difficult to veer from the path. We ask for this pressure because it is this pressure that purifies us, purifies our minds and our hearts, bending the curve of self-will toward the will of the Divine, toward devotion.

We've all experienced the transformative power of time, the great healer. Things that seem impossible today are the source of great laughter in the future, and what we do today can change our tomorrow. And, whether we believe it or not, what we do tomorrow can change yesterday. We can transform our stories, those things that defined us in the past and rewrite our destiny. This is the essential element of transformation—that we, ourselves, can be the agents of change within our own lives.

Kundalini Yoga inspired me to change everything. In fact, recently a friend was visiting and she said something that moved me in a way I hadn't anticipated. She said, "You are the most changed person I've ever known." It's taken all the elements, all these seeds of transformation, in order to affect this change in me: the fires of loss and the *tapas* of discipline; the pressure of community and the willingness to dress the part, even when I didn't feel like it; and time—lots of time. Nothing has happened overnight, except perhaps the gift of grace, the strength to say yes, and the willingness to agree to agree, to decide—and along with that decision came the opportunity to begin again.

We hope this newest collection of kriyas and meditations inspires you to begin your own personal transformation today! Practice something new or master something familiar with *Transformation: Seeds of Change for the Aquarian Age*, a two-volume series that brings the tools and technologies of Level Two Teacher Training to your fingertips.

The 86 kriyas and meditations in *Volume Two: Serving the Infinite* are drawn from across the entire Transformation: Level Two Teacher Training curriculum. Organized to facilitate your personal practice and deepen your experience of the Self, *Serving the Infinite* also helps you develop workshops, plan 6-week thematic courses, or assign individual sadhanas with ease. Using each chapter, individually, or combining topics gives you limitless possibilities.

Transformation is the key to success in the Aquarian Age. We hope this becomes just one of the many tools you keep by your side as you change and grow to meet the needs of the times.

Sat Purkh Kaur Khalsa
Editor & Creative Director
Kundalini Research Institute

TRANSFORMATION

INTRODUCTION

There is only one thing in life which is constant—change. Life, by definition, is animated and animation means movement. So if something is alive, it must continually change and transform—it must move. It is not a question of if we want to change or not, but where that change will take us. Where is this journey leading us?

If you practice Kundalini Yoga as taught by Yogi Bhajan®, chances are, at some point you saw the direction your life was taking and decided: "Hey, wait a minute, that's not where I wanted to go!" In that moment of awareness you decided to step off the endless, grinding wheel of karma, and begin your journey down the path of self-awareness.

Yogi Bhajan predicted that as the planet moves from the Piscean to the Aquarian Age, we would witness increasing internal and external turmoil, as old institutions collapsed and the human being became increasingly sensitive. He believed the ancient science of Kundalini Yoga would prove a remarkable technology to balance the glands, strengthen the nerves and help control the mind. But more than that, he believed it would deliver an experience of the Self that would help us not only survive, but also thrive in the coming Age.

I am blessed to have a job that takes me around the world. In my travels I am continually amazed by the technology of Kundalini Yoga, its boundlessness, unfettered by culture, race or society. I also get to witness Yogi Bhajan's predictions about this coming Age coming into being: the institutions of family, church, culture and society, which used to define us, and the course of our lives, are all breaking down and losing their influence on us. These institutions once told us who we were, who we could marry, what professions we could follow, how many children we could have. They defined our beliefs and values. They told us what was right and what was wrong, who was good and who was bad. As these outside institutions lose their control over our lives, two things can happen: we can experience a liberating sense of freedom or we can experience confusion and fear, overwhelmed by the unlimited choices and self-responsibility which confronts us.

Kundalini Yoga is the Yoga of Awareness. The perfect technology for these turbulent, uncertain times, its kriyas and meditations make us sensitive and aware of all our human facets. The sense of awareness opens us up to observe the myriad sensations, thoughts, feelings and desires of the little self, the ego, which constantly whirl through us. With this awareness, we begin to realize the impact they have on the direction of our lives, which takes us deeper, giving us an experience of the True Self whose clarity, calmness and peace are untouched by emotion and commotion. We begin to gain a deep understanding of our humanness and create a relationship between the projections of our ego and our True Self. On a very deep level, the Neutral Mind provides us with a profound experience of Self, so that we can release the pain and anger of the past, face the fear of the future, free ourselves from the chains of our karmic fate and connect ourselves with our spiritual destiny. In doing so, we redefine our identity in relation to our Soul, reestablish our beliefs on a foundation of experience and recreate our habits based on our values, which reflect our deepest Truth.

Through the experience of Self, we come to realize that for the past two thousand years we have had a distorted understanding of human nature. We are not human beings who've come here for a spiritual experience, but rather spirit, come into this life for a human experience. We are not sinful by nature. We are not separated from Heaven. Instead, we are souls whose essence is pure and whose nature is divine. The purpose of life's journey is to uncover that divine essence and experience *cherdi kala*, the ever-rising spirit that brings the peace and happiness of Heaven down to Earth.

"When you are not true to your body, and you have no relationship with your mind and you are not giving rest to your spirit, why would you think that everything should be all right? Forget about great spirituality and all those stories you might have heard: flying at night and descending from the Heavens. That is not the Age of Aquarius. The Age of Aquarius is the knowledge of the Self—willingly learning about the Self and being as devoted as you can be. Asking for yourself, "I am the grace of God, I am the creation of God"; knowing "If you cannot see God in all, you cannot see God at all"; understanding "Live to love and love to live." And when you love, doesn't matter how much time and space tests you, question not, you will win. Question, you lose." –Yogi Bhajan, March 27, 1997

This understanding reflects itself in the simple working principle of Kundalini Yoga: *Sat Nam, Wahe Guru.* Uncover your True Self, *Sat Nam*, connect with your divine essence and, in that moment, you will experience *Wahe Guru*, the pure joy and ecstasy of Being. Your destiny will open up to you and you will finally know true fulfillment.

Transformation: Seeds of Change for the Aquarian Age reflects this basic working principle. In *Volume One: Mastering the Self*, we have organized the Kundalini Yoga Kriyas and Meditations in thematic chapters to guide you on an inward journey toward self-discovery—*Sat Nam*. These tools can help you unlock your inner vitality and give you the strength to face your fear of change; observe, with clarity and neutrality, your habits and your mind's interactions with others; allow you to drop the pain of the past and channel the destructive force of anger into positive, personal transformation; clear and balance your chakras; recognize your own majesty and radiance; and create a deep and fulfilling relationship with your True Self.

In *Volume Two: Serving the Infinite*, we offer the tools to express that joy of experiencing the Self, *Wahe Guru*, and share it with the world around you—opening your heart, sharing your love, using your intuition, and listening deeply—so that you can serve the Infinite creation of the One who created you.

Tarn Taran Singh Khalsa
Director of the Aquarian Trainer Academy
Kundalini Research Institute
January 2010

TRANSFORMATION

CONTENTS

Before You Begin

Transformation: Serving the Infinite is intended for anyone currently practicing Kundalini Yoga as taught by Yogi Bhajan®. The Kriyas and Meditations included in this manual, however, are considered intermediate level. Some experience is not only recommended but assumed.

Beginning Your Practice—Tuning-In

The practice of Kundalini Yoga as taught by Yogi Bhajan® always begins by tuning-in. This simple practice aligns your mind, your spirit and your body to become alert and assert your will so that your practice will fulfill its intention. It's a simple bowing to your Higher Self and an alignment with the teacher within. The mantra is simple but it links you to a Golden Chain of teachers, an entire body of consciousness that guides and protects your practice: *Ong Namo Guru Dev Namo.* I bow to the Infinite, I bow to the Teacher within.

Ong   Na-mo   Gu- roo Dayv   Na- mo

How to End

Another tradition within Kundalini Yoga as taught by Yogi Bhajan® is a simple blessing known as The Long Time Sun song. Sung or simply recited at the end of your practice, it allows you to dedicate your practice to all those who've preserved and delivered these teachings so that you might have the experience of your Self. It is a simple prayer to bless yourself and others. It completes the practice and allows your entire discipline to become a prayer, in service to the good of all.

> May the long time sun shine upon you
> All love surround you
> And the pure light within you
> Guide your way on.
> Sat Nam.

Other Tips for a Successful Experience

Prepare for your practice by lining up all the elements that will elevate your experience: natural fiber clothing and head covering (cotton or linen), preferably white to increase your auric body; natural fiber mat, either cotton or wool; traditionally a sheep skin or other animal skin is used. If you have to use a rubber or petroleum-based mat, cover the surface with a cotton or wool blanket to protect and support your electromagnetic field. Clean air and fresh water also help support your practice.

Practice in Community

Kundalini Yoga cultivates group consciousness because group consciousness is the first step toward universal consciousness, which is the goal: transcend the ego and merge with Infinity. Therefore, find a teacher in your area. Studying the science of Kundalini Yoga with a KRI certified teacher will enhance your experience and deepen your understanding of kriya, mantra, breath and posture. If there isn't a teacher in your area, consider becoming a teacher yourself. *See our resources page for more information.*

Find a group to practice sadhana (daily spiritual routine) with, or establish a group sadhana yourself—in your home or community center. The Aquarian Sadhana was given by Yogi Bhajan to ground our practice now and into the Aquarian Age. Practicing with others increases the effects of sadhana exponentially. You heal others and others, in turn, heal you. (See *Kundalini Yoga Sadhana Guidelines*, 2nd Edition, available from the Kundalini Research Institute, for more information about creating your own sadhana and guidelines for practicing the Aquarian Sadhana.)

Come together as men and women and share your strength, ask for help when you need it, and laugh together as you participate in this game of life as you heal your Self, serve your community and lead throughout the Aquarian Age.

Pronunciation Guide

This simple guide to the vowel sounds in transliteration is for your convenience. More commonly used words are often spelled traditionally, for example, *Sat Nam, Wahe Guru,* or pranayam, even though you'll often see them written *Sat Naam, Whaa-hay Guroo,* and praanayaam, in order to clarify the pronunciation, especially in mantras. Gurbani is a very sophisticated sound system, and there are many other guidelines regarding consonant sounds and other rules of the language that are best conveyed through a direct student-teacher relationship. Further guidelines regarding pronunciation are available at www.kundaliniresearchinstitute.org.

a	hut
aa	mom
u	put, soot
oo	pool
i	fin
ee	feet
ai	let
ay	hay, rain
r	flick tongue on upper palate

CHAPTER ONE

PREPARING FOR
THE AQUARIAN AGE

SERVING THE INFINITE

Be the Lighthouse

"Meet the Age of Aquarius with strength, not weakness."[1]
–Yogi Bhajan

The Age of Aquarius is here. Are you prepared? We must ask ourselves: Are we ready to serve and uplift? Are we strong enough and prosperous enough, in spirit, to give without reservation? Do we have the vitality to carry not only ourselves but also others? Have we resolved our own duality so that our very presence is a blessing? Are we the teachers of the Aquarian Age—or are we not?

Yogi Bhajan called us to be the lighthouse: *"You have to go out, touch every heart. You have to go out to teach and touch every heart. . . . This Age we are going to face, everybody will be looking perfect on the outside but on the inside they are a living nervous wreck. . . . This plague of nervousness is going to touch every human mind, body and soul. At that time, you can create heavens: Teach, touch and spread the Word of the Guru. These are the three points to live by: live by them, live for them and die for them. Teach, touch and spread the Word."*[2]

We see it happening all around us. People unable to assimilate their emotions and anxieties, children unable to find balance among all the various forms of stimulation. There's too much information, too many options, and too little connection. People feel lost. In the midst of huge cities and in the hearts of small towns, people feel alone and lonely. But they don't have to. Our gift to them is to connect, first to their own inner awareness and then to one another. This is a teacher's blessing.

Learning to bless is one of our primary challenges as teachers. In order to bless, we must be a clear channel for the Infinite. Any remaining shadows must be swept away so that the clear light of consciousness can shine through. We have to break from our Piscean hypnotic trance and recharge ourselves for the Aquarian Age. In facing the challenge of tomorrow, we must deliver, we cannot fail.

Before we can bless others, we must learn to bless ourselves. This can be a daunting task. The negativity from our past or the lack of self-esteem from our childhood can make the thought of blessing ourselves untenable. To be able to bless all, we must see the God in all—even in ourselves. As Yogi Bhajan said: *"If you can't see God in all, you can't see God at all."* Meeting this challenge and overcoming this block becomes our greatest gift. In blessing ourselves, we learn to bless everyone.

The Aquarian Age is here. We need to be the lighthouse. We must be ready to lead, heal and serve; poke, provoke, confront—and above all elevate! Understand that I and you are we, and we are one. This is our gift and our challenge.

May we serve the Age with grace and strength and humility and may we deliver the legacy of these Teachings to all.

[1] © The Teachings of Yogi Bhajan, December 20, 1996
[2] © The Teachings of Yogi Bhajan, April 14, 1987

Recharge the Self for the Aquarian Age

Have an orange ready to eat after completing the set.

Sit in Easy Pose. Look at the tip of the nose.

1. Split the Mercury (pinkie) Finger and the Ego (thumb) keeping the three middle fingers together. Place the hands on each side of the head, palms facing forward. Make tiny circles with the hands. The right hand moves to the right and the left to the left. **26 minutes.**

After **6 minutes**, play **Har Har Har Har Gobinday** by Nirinjan Kaur.

Continue the meditation while listening to the mantra. This music manufactures prosperity. This mantra is a money-making machine. . . . Now you are entering a twilight zone in this exercise that you will not like; you may become insensitive to the movement; or you will be uncomfortable. The more powerfully you move, the more your breath will change and it will help.

Naturally you are beautiful. But by self-denial you become the victim of your own ugliness. Naturally you are wise. But by self-denial you become insane. By nature God must provide, through the law of prosperity, anything you need. But by your self-denial you create insecurity and you become poor. This exercise is going to change you inside out. You must do it sincerely. Win! Win! Win! Defeat the defeatism; depress the depression. You must claim the energy from within you; nobody is going to give you an injection from the outside. Change your magnetic field. Do it for your own sake! You want to be healthy, is that true? You want to have strength; you want to have intuition; you want to have tomorrow, don't give up. Push through these last few minutes. Push! Decide how much you love yourself now . . . give yourself a chance. I need your strength for tomorrow.

2. Put the right arm up at 60 degrees with the palm up, flat and parallel to the sky (the wrist is extended) and the left arm 60 degrees down toward the Earth, palm down and parallel to the Earth (with wrist extended). Together they create a diagonal line across the body. Arms are straight, with no bend in the elbow. **11 minutes.**

If you ate sattvic food, this wouldn't hurt you. But your two meals a day and your goodies, they are hurting you now.

Note: Clap your hands for a few seconds to transition to the next exercise.

Recharge the Self for the Aquarian Age

3. Reach the arms directly out in front of you, from the shoulders, with the palms up. Palms are flat and the arms are straight. Look at the tip of the nose. **5 minutes**.
Pray to Almighty God that he should come into the palm of your hand. Tell God to dance in the palm of your hand.

4. Place the hands in the lap. Sit straight like a sage. Do a self-hypnosis that you are a sage: A saint, a sage, a prophet. Don't worry what you are, or what you think you are, or what someone else thinks you are, think only:
    "I am the saint of the saint, the sage of the sage. I am the sage of the Age. I am I am."
    Go deep, into the center of the Earth. Drop deep into the center of the planet Earth. Sit like a powerhouse and personify as a Sage of this Age. (*The recording Meditation by Wahe Guru Kaur is played.*) I am Sage of the Age. **13 minutes**.

5. Breath of Fire. Wake up your body. Move the navel powerfully. Recharge yourself. **1 minute**. Relax.

6. Prayer Pose. Press the hands together at the center of the chest very hard. Inhale deep; hold tight and press hard. Cannon Breath exhale. **3 times**.

COMMENTS
In the Age of Aquarius you will not survive if you do not have self-power . . . not with money, outside environments, help, logic, reason, or anything . . . . The only thing which will survive in this Age is a person who has power to self-propel . . . otherwise, you will be eaten up by your own insanity. There is no way out. The heavens have changed, Earth has no option.

Balancing Mind & Heart Unto Infinity

MUDRA: Sit in Easy Pose with a straight spine. Bring the hands onto the chest so that the thumbs are tucked into the armpits. The thumbs press against the ribs. Rest the palms and fingers of each hand against the chest. Relax the elbows down by the sides.

BREATH & MANTRA: Pucker the lips and inhale deeply through the mouth with a whistle. Listen to the whistle sound of the inhalation as you mentally vibrate the sound: *So*. Completely exhale through the nose as you listen to the breath and mentally vibrate the sound *Hang*.
11 minutes.
So Hang means, "Infinity, I am Thou."

EYES: 1/10th open.

COMMENTS

This meditation balances the frequency and quality of the Heart Center. The Heart Center opens the potential for compassion and humility. Humanity is now going through a global transition into the Aquarian Age. We are preparing to have sovereignty over the service of the Universal force. This requires Universal Consciousness. There are two ways of developing Universal Consciousness: through hardship and time or through mantra. Mantra is the easier way, but the difficulty is that mantra opens the Heart Center and the mind has difficulty following the heart's frequency. It is through the understanding that comes from the heart that the mind can realize the concept that Infinity is within us.

Facing the Challenge of Tomorrow

1. Sit in Easy Pose with the arms straight out to the sides. The elbows are up at the same level as the shoulders and the palms face downward. Bend the elbows in so that the forearms and fingertips point straight forward. There will be a stretch felt in the armpits. Close the eyes and focus the closed eyes at the tip of the chin. Breathe slowly and deeply. Sit straight with the chin in and the chest out. **3 minutes**.

2. Remain in the same position as the first exercise but turn the palms facing up toward the ceiling. This will stretch the wrists. Do the best you can to make the palms turn upwards.
3 minutes.

3. Still in the same position, turn the palms so that they are facing out to the sides. The pinkie side of the hand is up and the thumb side of the hand is down. Keep the arms up at shoulder level and still focus the closed eyes at the center of the chin.
3 minutes.

TO END: Inhale, hold the breath, and squeeze all the muscles of the body. Exhale and repeat two more times. Relax.

4. Stand up and dance to the music such as *Bangara Drums* by Matamandir Singh. **11 minutes**. For the last minute, begin clapping the hands together.

Breaking the Piscean Hypnotic Trance

Sit in a comfortable, meditative posture.

MUDRA: Bring the hands into fists with the thumb over the middle finger. Place them in front of the chest about six inches apart. Point the Jupiter (index) finger up to the sky.

1. Begin moving the hands alternately, in a precise way, forward and back. Do this in a mechanical, slow, almost jerky, motion— with a steady, even cadence. Do it with full awareness. **6 minutes.**

2. Continue the movement of the hands and bring the eyes to the tip of the nose. **3 minutes.**

3. Continue the movement and begin chanting "*Thou*" with each movement of the hands. **4 minutes.**

4. Close the eyes. Still the hands and relax them down. Come to absolute silence and stillness. Practice nonexistence. For a moment forget who you are. **6 minutes.**

TO END: Inhale deep and stretch the arms up. Exhale. Inhale deep and twist to the left. Stretch. Exhale in the center. Inhale deep and twist to the right. Stretch. Exhale in the center and relax.

Meditation for the Positive Mind

Sit with an erect spine. Curl the Sun (ring) finger and Mercury (pinkie) finger into each palm. Bend the thumbs over top of them to lock them into place. Keep the first two fingers (Jupiter and Saturn) straight. Bring the arms so the elbows are by the sides, and the hands are by the shoulders with the two fingers of each hand pointing straight up. Bring the forearms and hands forward to an angle of 30 degrees from the vertical. Press the shoulders and elbows back firmly but comfortably. The palms face forward.

EYES: Close the eyes. Roll the eyes up gently and concentrate at the Brow Point—the Third Eye area—between the eyebrows.

BREATH: Create a steady, slow, deep and complete breath.

MANTRA: Mentally pulse rhythmically from the Brow Point out to Infinity the sounds:

Saa Taa Naa Maa

Saa is Infinity. Taa is Life. Naa is Death. Maa is Rebirth/Transformation.

This describes the cycle of life and brings a total mental balance to the psyche. The entire mantra means, "I meditate on Truth, Truth that I am."

TIME: Practice for **11 to 62 minutes.**

TO END: Inhale deeply and exhale 3 times. Then open and close the fists several times. Relax.

COMMENTS

Try practicing this meditation for 40 days. During that time eat lightly and speak only truth directly from your heart. This practice opens the Heart Center and the feelings of the positive self. It is a gesture of happiness. It has a great history and is said to have been practiced by many great and wise spiritual leaders including Buddha and Christ. The hand mudra became a symbol for blessing and prosperity.

Meditation for Blessing

Sit in Easy Pose with a straight spine, chin in, chest out.

MUDRA: Bend the Sun (ring) and Mercury (pinkie) fingers into the palm, and hold them down with the thumb. Extend the Jupiter (index) and Saturn (middle) fingers out straight. Extend the arms straight out to the sides, no bend to the elbows, right hand palm up toward the ceiling, and left hand palm down toward the ground. Keep them up at shoulder level, parallel to the ground.

EYES: Gaze at the tip of the nose.

MANTRA:

> *Whaa-Hay Guroo, Whaa-Hay Guroo*
> *Whaa-Hay Guroo, Whaa-Hay Jeeo*

The recording by Gianiji which Yogi Bhajan refers to as the "Paris Tape" is used.

TIME: **11 minutes**.

TO END: Inhale, hold the breath, and concentrate on all the vertebrae of the spine, starting from the base, and going all the way up to the neck, pulling them into the spine, tightening them into place. Hold the breath 20 seconds. Cannon-fire the breath out. Repeat 3 times total, expanding the lungs wider on each inhale, and tightening the spine with all your power each time. Relax.

COMMENTS

The spine must not move. As you look at the tip of the nose, your forehead will begin to feel like lead. This is a pressure which is helping to develop the frontal lobe, which controls the personality. Just go through it and conquer the pain. The hands must be in balance with the spine because with these hands you will heal. You need that touch, so let the energy flow.

The words you are singing mean, "God, take me from darkness to light." It's an affirmation, a prayer. If the exercise becomes very painful, try singing along with the tape, copying the words. It may help. Keep the arms in balance, the spine straight and stretch the arms out tightly—it will make it easier. Keep the posture perfect in the final 2 minutes—it is a very critical time.

This meditation will powerfully develop the frontal brain. Yogi Bhajan gave it to create balance under the pressure of the New Age shift. We will be assaulted with a new level of sensitivity and a sense of disconnection and fatigue if we do not control the frontal lobe, sort through thoughts, and counter the reactive splits and personalities we generate in our subconscious.

Developing the Qualities of a Leader

Sit on the heels with a straight spine.

MUDRA & MOVEMENT: Stretch the arms straight out in front, parallel to the ground. The palms are flat and facing the ground; the fingers point straight forward. The arms will be shoulder-width apart. As you chant the mantra alternately raise the arms up to 60 degrees and then return them to their original position as follows:

Aadays	*raise arms up to 60 degrees*
Tisai	*arms straight out in front*
Aadays	*up to 60 degrees*
Aad	*straight in front*
Aneel	*up to 60 degrees*
Anaad	*straight in front*
Anaahat	*up to 60 degrees*
Jug-jug	*straight in front*
Ayko	*up to 60 degrees*
Vays	*straight in front*

The mantra is spoken in a continuous monotone, in a precise beat with a projection of strength. Each word is spoken individually with a slight pause between each word, except *Jug-jug*, which is run together as one word. Speak from the Navel Point.

TIME: Continue for 31 minutes.

TO END: Inhale deeply. Relax.

COMMENTS

This meditation rids you of fears and split personalities, allowing the qualities of critical assessment and responsibility for action to develop and be balanced, as they are in great leaders. A leader must look ahead and beyond the surface. There is a mental habit to constantly assess everything, even in the midst of great absorption to the task at hand, allowing you to hold each boundary and division of role with integrity and accuracy. The Neutral Mind helps you evaluate each person and each resource that comes to you for what it can and cannot do. The ability to see beyond the surface lets you call on the talent and hidden potential of each person. That builds trust and loyalty when used with respect for each person and with the focus that moves everyone to reach a goal. Passion applied in the right place is inspiration, but passion reacting without a sense of place or timing is not good leadership, even if it stirs people.

Meditation for an Invincible Spirit

POSTURE: Sit in Easy Pose with a straight spine, and engage Neck Lock.

MUDRA: Left hand is in Gyan Mudra resting on the knee with the arm straight. Raise the right hand to about 12 inches in front of the chest, holding the mantra sheet and concentrating on the written words as you chant. If you don't have a mantra sheet, angle your hand as if you were reading a sheet of paper, with the palm open and the wrist straight.*

EYES: Apply Neck Lock and look down the nose to see the mantra sheet or the palm. When he gave this meditation, Yogi Bhajan asked us to focus the eyes, to pay attention and not drift. If you do not have the page to read from, use the palm but continue to focus.

MANTRA: The mantra is The Mantra for the Aquarian Age.
a) Chant with Nirinjan Kaur's *Aquarian March*. **7 minutes** (27 minutes for a 31-minute practice.)
b) Continue chanting, close the eyes and place the hands on the Heart Center, left palm on the heart, right palm resting on the left hand. Press the hands firmly into the chest. Press hard for **2 minutes**.
c) Keep your hands on the heart and begin to whisper the mantra. Whisper powerfully. **1 minute**.
d) Chant without the music for **30 seconds**. Inhale, exhale and relax.

Sat Siree Siree Akaal
Truth, Projective Prosperity & Greatness, Great Undying One Who Knows No Death
Siree Akaal Mahaa Akaal
Great Undying One Who Knows No Death, Infinite Who Is Deathless
Mahaa Akaal Sat Naam
Infinite Who Is Deathless, Truth as Identity; or Identity of All That Is
Akaal Moorat Whaa-Hay Guroo
Embodied Form or Image of the Infinite, The Ecstatic Totality of God & Existence

TIME: **11–31 minutes**.

COMMENTS

In the face of any great change, we confront three destructive impulses: to be alone and withdrawn, to deny or fantasize about the future, and to live with greed or scarcity instead of prosperity. This mantra counters these tendencies and instills the mind with courage and caliber. Focus on the movement of the tongue and the sensation of the sound as it creates a time and space.

There is a subtle difference in the meaning of the words "*Siri*" and "*Maha.*" "Great (*Siri*)" still has a touch of finiteness; "Infinite (*Maha*)" has no finiteness or form.

* Ideally, you would print the mantra on a sheet of paper and read the mantra as you chant. This is available from KRI for you to download.

CHAPTER TWO

INTUITION & INSIGHT

SERVING THE INFINITE

Our Natural Faculty of Intuition

If God is our Creator, then He has been very gracious to us, because He has created us with a brain that has two hemispheres. Each hemisphere allows us to understand and comprehend the universe in a completely different way. The left side of the brain is logical, linear, deductive, and rational—it is a great tool to understand the mechanics of time and space in the material world we exist in. The right side of the brain is intuitive, spatial, associational—and through it we can transcend time and space and connect ourselves with the subtle realms of existence that connect the material world with its spiritual source.

As Westerners we are well trained in left-brain thinking. We function well in this material world because of our ability to understand and manipulate time and space. But we have almost no training at all in the use of the right side of the brain. This makes us very suspicious of our intuitive impulses. We don't trust anything we can't perceive with our five senses or deduce from our rational mind. Everything else is just hocus-pocus or mysterious, and we either dismiss it straight out or approach it with great skepticism. Even to admit that it might have some validity makes us very uneasy.

This is unfortunate because what we loose is a depth and dimension that can add a richness to the quality of our lives. It confines us to the finite, material realm of existence. Our horizon is only as far as our life span. It instills in us a fear and dread of death, which haunts us throughout our lives.

But there is another more immediate and practical reason for developing our intuitive faculty.

We are currently experiencing the transition from the Piscean Age into the Aquarian Age, and, at the same time, we are experiencing the Information Revolution.

In the last 2,000 years access to information was key to success in life. No matter if you sought worldly or spiritual success, the critical success factor was sourcing, and often, protecting, information. In the competition of life, whoever held the information had the edge. In the next 2,000 years there will be no secrets. Information will be transparent and readily available to all. The critical success factor will be how to digest it and utilize it.

We are already being bombarded and at times overwhelmed with information. Just think about this in terms of yoga. If you lived in the West 1,000 years ago and by some coincidence heard about yoga, and wanted to find out more about it, you would have had to travel thousands of miles across mountains, seas and deserts just to learn how to suspend your breath and focus at your Third Eye. A hundred years ago, you would have had to search in the most occult bookstores in London to maybe find one book. Thirty years ago, if you visited an esoteric bookstore you could sweep up a number of books on yoga. Today you find yoga tips on the cover of women's magazines at the checkout stand of the grocery store. Any bookstore will have a large stock of books on yoga and if you go to an esoteric bookstore you will find rooms full to overflowing with books on yoga. But if you really want to be overwhelmed, just type "yoga" into any search engine on your computer. How do you sort through all this information? Determine what is of interest to you? Have the time to study and test out its practice and evaluate its experience? This same phenomenon confronts us in all aspects of our lives. This overload is only going to get worse.

We will be completely bombarded with information. So to succeed, or merely survive, will not have to do with what or how much information you have, but rather with your ability to process it and use it.

Our left-brain is struggling fiercely to keep up using its logical, linear approach. We have time management, multi-tasking, speed-reading, super learning .... but there is no way even the most developed left-brain can keep up; it will eventually become overwhelmed and burn out.

So in order to process all this information, we need to develop the right side of the brain, to cultivate our intuition.

Yogi Bhajan says: *"As a human being, by nature, you have the capacity for a very deep understanding and sensitivity. Your mind has the faculty to analyze everything in the shortest possible time, so short it can't even be measured. This faculty is called intuition."*

(81 Facets of Mind page 8)

Intuition is a faculty every human is born with. We experience intuitive impulses all the time. But in the West our ignorance and suspicion have led us to build up protective barriers against these impulses. Kundalini Yoga provides us many tools with which we can learn to recognize, access, train and utilize this natural faculty.

Four Stroke Breath to Build Intuition

Sit in a comfortable seated position.

MUDRA: Place the hands together in Prayer Pose. Keep the Jupiter (index) fingers extended as you interlock the other fingers to clasp the two hands together. Cross the thumbs. Place the mudra a little below your nose where you can look at the tips of the Jupiter fingers through the one-tenth opening of your eyes.

EYES: The eyes are 1/10th open.

BREATH: Inhale in four powerful strokes through the "O" mouth (1 stroke per second = 4 second inhale) and exhale in one powerful stroke through the nose (1 second).

TIME: Continue for **16 minutes**.

TO END: Sit straight. Inhale, hold the breath 20 seconds, and stretch the arms out to the sides, palms facing upward. This will give you power to balance the central spinal column. Exhale. Inhale deep, hold the breath 20 seconds, and stretch the arms horizontally and stretch the spine vertically. Make a T-square. Exhale. Inhale deep, hold the breath 20 seconds, and open up the fingers, making them like steel. Squeeze your entire energy and bring it into your arms. Exhale and relax.

COMMENTS

"Whosoever does best, will get the best experience. I can't do this for you, I can only tell you what to do. Use your own diaphragm, move your own central (channel), open up your own chakras, achieve your own results. These exercises are time bound. Within that time you should achieve a sensory system. Take a heavy stroke through the mouth and push it out through the nose. In the Aquarian Age intuition will be the principle of identity. This is a little meditation to see how well we can tell our own pituitary to work for us. . . . You must know reality by intuition. Not by knowledge. By the time reality becomes knowledge, it's too late." —Yogi Bhajan

Inner Assessment

PART ONE

TO KNOW YOUR INNER BALANCE

Sit in Easy Pose, with eyes closed, focusing at the Third Eye Point. Bring the hands into Prayer Pose at the center of the chest. Slide the left hand upward until it is higher than the right, with the left palm facing to the right side. The right palm faces left and touches the left arm just below the wrist. Breathe as long and slowly as you can.
3-11 minutes.

PART TWO

TO KNOW YOUR INNER PROJECTION

Sit in Easy Pose with the eyes closed, focusing at the Third Eye Point. The thumbs are hooked into the hollows on either side of the bridge of the nose. Slowly close the palms into Prayer Pose, closing from the bottom of the side of the palms upward, touching the sides of the fingers last. Hold this position. Breathe as long and slowly as you can.
3-11 minutes.

PART THREE

TO KNOW YOUR INNER STRENGTH

Sit in Easy Pose with the eyes closed, focusing at the Third Eye Point. Breathe as long and slowly as you can. Place your right hand over your left at your Heart Center and press as hard as you can, maintaining the pressure throughout the meditation.
3-11 minutes.

Ghost Kriya
Clearing & Opening to Intuition

1. Chin is slightly up so that the Moon Center (at the chin) does not cross vertical. Bring the arms up with the palms facing each other. Stretch the arms up and move the arms together in a figure eight; move lightly, keeping the arms stretched up. Open the armpit. The torso rocks forward and back in concert with the arms. Close the eyes and see the darkness. Approximately **30 minutes**.

Become ghosts. You can get rid of all of your inner ghosts if you do it right. The best way to get rid of the ghost is to become one. Get into it! Become it! Feel you are a ghost, flying in the air across the dazzling light. [After about 11 minutes] Now start flying through the scorching heat of the desert; flying through the Sahara; start going through it. Go through the heat and the vastness of it. Move with great strength. There is a huge desert that you must go through. You are now creating a field of your own psyche, absolutely delightful, transparent body is that of a ghost and you are going through the depth of all the deserts in the world: Gobi, Sahara, etc. Wherever your memory or subconscious takes you; get into your own vast desert! Move in the rhythmic eight of the subtle self.

After about 15 minutes, stretch the arms up even higher, toward vertical, and continue moving. Keep your armpit completely stretched and open.

Fly above the clouds, directly beneath the sun. You have a lot of cloudiness in life and you must get rid of it. Fly above the clouds! Work it out! Keep on ghosting yourself. Unload the cloudiness. Unload the tears. Now please enter a lush, green rainforest. Be kind to your beauty, your bountifulness, blissfulness. This movement forces your subconscious to unload. Be happy; do it happily. Cool yourself through the lush, green rainforest. You can clear out your previous 25 incarnations. Now move into a long range of mountains, totally filled with snow, white and bright and shining where calmness and quietness where sound resounds a million times. Move in that most beautiful eight of the subtle body. It will help you; it will cure you. Fly over the beautiful white snow-covered mountains. Keep going! From one peak to another peak, travel from top to top. Keep ghosting. Keep flying. Keep the armpit open; that's the only thing that is working. Let us end the haunting! Move!

TO END: Inhale deep and stretch the arms up and become wide, become big. Exhale. Repeat.

Ghost Kriya
Clearing & Opening to Intuition

2. Exhale the hands into the lap and do not open the eyes. Keep the hands in your lap, with the right hand resting in the left, palms up. Sit straight and meditate. Gong is played. **14 minutes**.

Go to your school days. From First Grade on. What did you think you could be? What did you want to be—then? What was the most imaginative profile of yourself in the 1st, 2nd, 3rd, 4th, 5th, 6th 7th, 8th, 9th, 10th, 11th and 12th grades? Review it in detail. As ghost knows all, you know all. As you remember, try to be that and your ghost will eat it up and you shall be free. Give your memories to the ghost.

3. Open the mouth and begin breathing through the mouth. Teeth should not touch. Gong continues. **2 minutes**.

4. Breath through the nostrils as slowly as you can. Keep the mouth open; the teeth should not touch. Gong continues. **3 minutes**.

Good and bad? You are all good. You are made in the image of God. You are the prana of God. The light of God.

5. Sing with the mantra *Rakhe Rakhanhaar. (Singh Kaur's version was used in class.)* Copy the sounds. Chant with the tongue. Consciously use the tongue. Press the palate with the tongue. **6 minutes**.

Even though many of you may not know the words, all that needs to happen is to press the tongue on the upper palate. When you stiffen the tongue and utter the Word, if the tongue is pressed against the palate with these sounds, you will be unloading your difficulty, pain, disease. Nothing has worked better than the Word of God. These sounds are a combined permutation and combination of the tongue and palate. I want the tongue to be tough and stiff. Each word has to be conscious. I don't want these memories you have unloaded to come back; I want them to be gone forever.

6. Wake up in the morning to the sound of the mantra *Rakhe Rakhanhaar.* Repeat with a tough tongue for a few minutes. Watch that day. Observe what happens.

(See page 27 for the words of the mantra Rakhe Rakhanhaar.)

Becoming Intuitive

1. Place the left hand over the heart. Bend the right elbow, point the Jupiter (index) finger upward, with the thumb locking down the other three fingers. Consciously keep the spine very straight and pulled up, with no weight on the buttocks. The eyes are closed. Inhale slowly and deeply through the nose, hold your breath, and then exhale slowly with a whistle through the mouth. **7 minutes**. Inhale deeply and shift position.

Imagine that something very pure and divine in you is calling. Reach out and make contact with your own Infinity. Create a feeling of being exalted by your own self.

2. Put your right hand either slightly above or just touching your head. Bend the left elbow. Point the Jupiter (index) finger upward, with the thumb locking down the other three fingers. Keep the spine pulled up straight. This is very important for the gray matter of the brain. Close your eyes and continue the breath from Exercise One. **4 minutes**.

3. Stretch the arms over the head with the hands together in Prayer Pose. Keep the spine straight and stretch up from the armpits. Continue the breath. You are consciously recirculating your energy to give your body new life. **2 1/2 minutes**.

Becoming Intuitive

4. Put the right hand over the left at the Heart Center. Sit and relax. Play Singh Kaur's recording of *Rakhe Rakhanhaar*. Listen, relax, breathe, and be. **3 minutes.**

5. Inhale deeply and press your hands against the Navel Point. Rhythmically chant **Har**. With each recitation, press the Navel Point forcefully with your hands. The eyes are closed. **3 minutes.**
(Simran Kaur's Tantric Har recording is excellent for this.)

TO END: Come into elbow lock position. The elbows are bent, with each hand grasping the opposite elbow. The arms are held parallel to the ground at shoulder height. Inhale, hold your breath 5-10 seconds, squeeze the spine, and tighten all the muscles of the body. Exhale. Repeat this sequence two more times.

COMMENTS
These exercises gently work on the pituitary. They recharge and enrich your energy and counteract frustration, depression, and computer sicknesses.

Make Your Mind Sensitive

Sit with a straight spine in Easy Pose.

1. Eyes are at the tip of nose. Make a fist of the right hand, extend the index finger straight up with the thumb over the middle finger. Place the hand in front of the right shoulder, with the closed palm facing the left. Keep the extended finger straight and stiff. The left hand is in Gyan Mudra. Breathe long and deep. **7 minutes**.

TO END: Maintaining the mudra, slowly begin to raise your right hand over your head, and inhale very deeply. Stretch and suspend the breath. Exhale. Repeat twice more. Relax.

Within 3 to 5 minutes you should feel the energy flowing through you. Rishi Dusht Daman experimented his whole life, 120 years, to find this simple truth which you are practicing right now. His realization was that if one can enforce the tip of his Jupiter finger into steel stiffness, he can grab from the universe the Jupiter energy; and If by the optical nerve, he can totally shut off the mind to misbehave, it will create a basic pattern of intuition. If you change the eyes for a second, you must start again from the beginning.

BREAK: Talk to your neighbor. You must talk—about anything—but don't meditate, don't relax, talk. **5 minutes**.

2. Still in Easy Pose. Spread the fingers of the left hand as far apart as possible, with equal distance between each finger. Place the palm flat against the center of the chest. Extend the right arm up at a 60 degree angle and to the right about 30-45 degrees with the palm facing down and fingers spread wide. The elbow is locked and straight. Eyes are focused on the tip of nose. Breathe long and deep. **7 minutes**.

Make Your Mind Sensitive

TO END: Maintain the posture and inhale deep. Hold and stretch that arm out. Exhale. Repeat twice more and relax.

"Forget about yourself. My right hand is at 60 degrees; armpit must not be straight, must not be higher than 60 degrees. The nervous center of the sympathetic, parasympathetic, and action system is in the armpit, remember that! Armpit is the most important part of the body, and you neglect it the most. You think it is just a joint. It is not. The entire nervous system is based in the armpit. . . . Now you are getting all the five energies at the same time. The thumb represents the id, the ego. Then there is Jupiter, Saturn, Sun and Mercury. Five main planets, underneath is the planet Mars, and the Venus is under the id. . . . So please understand, you are almost in control of your total energy. This exercise adjusts the ribs automatically."
BREAK: Talk to your neighbor. You must talk—about anything—but don't meditate, don't relax, talk. **5 minutes.**

3. *Sodarshan Kriya*: Bring the hands into fists in front of the chest, at shoulder level—about 6-9 inches apart. The fists are facing each other. Extend the two Jupiter fingers straight up. Begin rotating the Jupiter fingers in circles toward each other. (The left finger moves clockwise and the right finger moves counterclockwise.) Move only the fingers, not the hands. Do a quick Breath of Fire. **7 minutes.**

TO END: Inhale deep, stretch the hands very tight, over the head, and hold. Exhale with a cannon fire breath through the mouth. Repeat twice more and relax.

We are hitting at the chemistry of our blood formation. It's so important. What you are doing is much healthier than taking two tons of vitamins. It is not guaranteed, but it will avoid cancer in your body. It is a help to that precaution. You can make your body disease free by doing it for 7 minutes. I did it myself to heal myself. It is called Sodarshan Kriya. It is very important. You will see Lord Vishnu raising one finger and moving it. He moves so fast that the whole wheel moves with it. It is symbolic, but we can learn from that. We are not going to become Lord Vishnu. Neither do we want to raise the whole wheel. All we want is to change the entire Sun and Sun means blood.

BREAK: Talk to your neighbor. You must talk—about anything—but don't meditate, don't relax, talk. **5 minutes.**

Kriya to Know Through Intuition

Sit in Easy Pose with the spine straight.

1. The left elbow is bent, palm flat facing the floor, in front of the Heart Center. The right arm is extended out to the front at a 60 degree angle. Close the eyes and breathe slowly and honestly. (Work up to breathing only one breath per minute.) Feel the Divine Presence around you. **11 minutes**.

TO END: Stay in the position, inhale deep, hold the breath 10 seconds as you tighten all the muscles of the body. Exhale. Repeat 2 more times. Relax, roll your shoulders, stretch your arms and rib cage.

2. Extend the arms straight out in front of the chest with the palms touching and the thumbs locked over each other. Close the eyes and whistle a song of your choice. **7 minutes**.
This posture affects the parathyroid and you may feel a pressure in your neck.

3. Put the hands in Lotus Mudra at eye level. Relax the entire body but hold the hand position firmly. Close the eyes for **3 minutes**.
This is an intertwined action when one part of the body in a confined posture becomes the antenna and the rest of the body is relaxed to receive.

TO END: Inhale and clasp the hands in front of the Heart Center and press as hard as you can. Exhale and repeat 2 more times.
Then relax, talk, and ground yourself for a few moments.

COMMENTS

This kriya develops your ability to open to the Unknown through intuition and sensitivity. The First Exercise done with the One Minute Breath links the Heart Center, the Arcline and your projection. Feel your magnetic field and Aura as you meditate. Establish an open, sensitive and unlimited field. In Exercise Two the Sixth Chakra is stimulated into action with the sound of the high pitched whistle. The sound relaxes and opens. The hand lock enhances neutrality. The Third Exercise is the fulcrum. You create a polarity between the fixed hand position, like antennae, and the relaxed cells of the rest of the body. You welcome and receive the information and intuition from the known and Unknown. It is an excellent kriya to prepare for powerful prayer and to develop intuition.

Self-Hypnosis to Develop Intuition

Sit in a comfortable meditative posture.

MUDRA: Bring the hands up by the sides, palms up toward the ceiling, elbows at your sides. Place the thumb and Mercury (pinkie) finger together in Buddhi Mudra.

EYES: Close the eyes. Focus on the back of the neck. Look through the back of the neck.

BREATH: Breathe long and deep.
"Longer the breath; longer the life." —Yogi Bhajan

MANTRA:

Guru Guru Wahe Guru, Guru Ram Das Guru
Singh Kaur's recording is played.

TIME: **11-22 minutes.**

TO END:
Inhale deep. Press the hands into the chest. Press hard. 30 seconds. Exhale.
Inhale deep. Press the hands into the Navel. Press hard. 30 seconds. Exhale.
Inhale deep and fold the hands at the heart in Prayer Pose, and press the hands together—hard. 30 seconds. Exhale and relax.

Meditation for Balanced Creativity

Sit in a comfortable meditative posture.

Spread the fingers of each hand wide with the palms facing up. Touch the sides of the tips of the Sun (ring) fingers together. The hands will slightly overlap with the left little finger lower than the right. No fingers other than the Sun fingers should be touching. Place the mudra at the level of the Heart Center.

EYES: Look down toward the fingers.

MANTRA: Mentally chant:

Saa Taa Naa Maa

Chant as you would in Kirtan Kriya, mentally pulsing the thumb tip with each fingertip in sequence.

BREATH: Breathe slow and deep, four times a minute or less.

TIME: **31 minutes**.

COMMENTS

This meditation gives you extraordinary sensitivity to sensations, emotions, and impressions from nature and other people. Its basic urge is to create, elaborate, and express each sensation. Too strong, you seem bewitched by special people, places, and things. You see a richness that pulls you powerfully towards a sensation. You take risks, flirt with addictions, and find only positive impacts in tragedy, intense experiences, and change. You underestimate the future impact of your present actions and explorations. Too weak, you lack spontaneous joy from all that happens and retreat to internal imagination to feel good. You suspect the passion you see in others has some other motive than stimulation or pleasure. You try to moderate your own desire to safe levels. Balanced, you explore every feeling by creating something to experience, to amplify, or to repeat. It is concerned with proportions, blends, and how to utilize what it senses. It is open to all opinions and loves diversity. Curiosity, wonder, and impatience are frequent moods for this part of your character. Your life becomes a work of art or an idiosyncratic piece of work. Moderation and dedication are essential.

Guidance Meditation

Sit in Easy Pose with the spine straight.

EYES: Closed.

MANTRA & MOVEMENT: Meditate to the music of **Rakhe Rakhanhaar** with the following movements:

1. Bring the arms up and hold opposite forearms near the elbows. Inhale in 8 parts, gently swinging the arms from side to side in rhythm with the breath and to the beat of the music (as if rocking a baby).

2. Exhale, lowering the arms to Gyan Mudra on knees. Continue inhaling and exhaling to the music at your own pace.

TIME: **31 minutes**.

Rakhay rakhanhaar aap ubaarian
Gur kee pairee paa-eh kaaj savaarian
Hoaa aap dayaal manho na visaarian
Saadh janaa kai sang bhavjal taarian
Saakat nindak dusht khin maa-eh bidaarian
Tis saahib kee tayk naanak manai maa-eh
Jis simrat sukh ho-eh saglay dookh jaa-eh

God Himself is looking out for me,
Gives me the light, and takes care of my affairs.
God is merciful, and never forgets me.
God guides me, giving me good people to help me.
God does not allow any harm to come to me.
I take comfort in the thought of God.
When I remember God, I feel peaceful and happy and
  all my pain departs.

EXPERIENCING
THE NAAD

SERVING THE INFINITE

Singing the Song of Our Soul

"The root word is 'aad.' You can play it any way you want, it will become music. To us it is rhythmical – Naad. The most beautiful instrument of all instruments is within us." –Yogi Bhajan

Every morning we begin the Aquarian Sadhana with Guru Nanak's beautiful Song of the Soul, *Jap Ji*. It begins with the Mul Mantra, describing the experience of the living Divinity that is being human: *Sat Nam*, one who lives to their highest potential, expressing their True Self, at one with the One, free from fear and anger, unborn and dying, absolutely complete. Every time I read the Mul Mantra I get the shivers and think "Wow! That's who I really am when I live to my true potential!" But that thought is immediately followed by, "Ok, that's nice, but how do I get from here to there?" Nanak answers: "Surrender the will, the wants and needs of your little ego-defined self to the Will of God and live the Destiny of your Soul." And again I think, "Yeah, that's it!" Only to be confronted with the question, "Well, how do I know, from all those voices in my head, which one is the voice of my Soul?" And once again Nanak has the answer: *Sunni-ai.* "Listen!" He goes on and on, for pages and pages, about the benefits that come to the one who deeply listens.

Kundalini Yoga is the Yoga of Awareness; and awareness comes through *Sunni-ai,* deep listening. In every Kundalini Yoga class we practice listening. We listen to our body, our thoughts, our emotions and our desires. We listen to anger, doubt and fear released from the subconscious. We listen to calm, peace and joy when we connect with our Soul. We listen to the Negative and Positive Minds in their endless debate, and hopefully we

get a chance to listen to our Neutral Mind resolve their duality with intuitive understanding.

Listening is what yoga is really all about. The oldest, most classic text, Patanjali's Eight Limbs of Yoga is all about stilling the waves of the mind, that is—how do we lower the constant noise level of the ego's commotions and emotions? How do we still the rantings and ravings of the monkey mind so that we can clearly discern the voice of the Soul? He begins with the *Yamas* which, like the Ten Commandments, are guidelines for harmonious relationships with others. Then he moves to the *Niyamas*, which tell us how to be in right relationship with ourselves.

Next we quiet the body by cleansing the organs and balancing the glands through asanas. Then we learn to control the breath, and begin to calm the mind through Pranayam. *Pratyahar* lowers the noise level even further by neutralizing the inputs from the sense organs. Now we get to work directly with the mind, learning to concentrate the flow of thought patterns, *Dhyana*, to achieve the state of true meditation, *Dharana*. Here we experience the Meditative Mind and the stillness within that we call *Shuniya*. In the state of *Shuniya*, where we are no longer distracted by the noise of the emotions rising from the subconscious, or controlled by our ego's need to defend itself, we can truly, deeply, honestly and neutrally listen. We can be truly aware of what is going on beneath the surface noise of our inner struggles and begin to listen to our Soul, understand God's Will for us, and see the path we need to follow in order to fulfill our Soul's Destiny. Through listening we can begin to sing our world into existence and express the song of our Soul—this is *Naad*.

The kriyas in this chapter take you into deep listening and an experience of the Sound Current which is the Shabd Guru. Working with the Shabd Guru is the fastest way to cut through the ego's games and find the truth that already lies deep within you. Listen, chant and sing—transform and unfold the soul's true longing to be one with the One.

Finding Happiness & Peace Within

Sit is Easy Pose with the spine straight, chin in and chest out. Jalandhar Bandh is especially important for this meditation.

1. Begin chanting **Ong** in the long form so that it takes approximately 10 seconds to chant one time. Chant though the conch, focusing at the Third Eye Point, making the sound nasal. The mouth is slightly open and the breath comes only out of the nostrils. Chant in this manner **5 times**.

2. Then gradually begin to chant **Ong** faster so that you are chanting one **Ong** every 3-5 seconds. Mouth is slightly open, and sound is created by opening and closing the back of the throat, focusing and vibrating the Brow Point. Start with **1 minute** of rapid **Ong** and gradually work up to **2 minutes**.

COMMENTS

"Practice it, it will set your brain, if you do it correctly. If you start to cough, allow it, because it is just your thyroid adjusting to the pressure. The thyroid is responsible for beauty and for keeping you young. Chanting this sound correctly gives power, beauty, and youth.

"There is no word 'Om.' Neither 'Aum.' Actually the sound 'Om' is the sound of the conch, which can only be created. It cannot be written and it cannot be expressed. It is the sound of Infinity (in Formlessness). When this starts working, even the loincloth is lost. It frees the man of all possessions.

"Ong is never chanted though the mouth, it comes through the central nerve channel, the Sushmana, which is the tip of the nose. It brings out from you the breath like fire. Ong is the sound that man found out of the conch where he put in the breath of life. Sound of the conch is an expanded Ong. When a disciple or seeker practices at the center of the nose, his entire brain gets a very specific vibration and then the nectar starts coming.

"Through time man started writing about the chanting of Ong and reading about it, but not practicing it. The result was that he eventually forgot what the sound is and then he became a shopper. He went from one place to another, to another, to another. He went from one person to another person to another person, asking, begging for happiness. He went from one religion to another, from one place to another, from one house to another, just asking for peace. He forgot that what he is asking for is within himself."   —Yogi Bhajan

Aad Naad Kriya

Sit with a straight spine in Easy Pose.

MUDRA: Interlock the fingers with the right index finger on top of the left index finger. The heels of the hands are joined and the thumbs are together and stretched back so that they point straight up. Relax the arms down with the elbows bent. The forearms are pulled up and in toward the chest until the hands are positioned in front of the chest between the solar plexus and the heart. Keep the thumbs stretched back.

EYES: Eyes are closed.

BREATH: Deeply inhale.

MANTRA: Chant the following mantra:

Raa Raa Raa Raa
Maa Maa Maa Maa
Saa Saa Saa Sat
Haree Har Haree Har

TIME: **11 minutes.** You can extend the time to 31 or 62 minutes.

TO END: End with a deep inhale, suspend the breath at least 15 seconds. Exhale through the mouth. Repeat 3 times.

Antar Naad Meditation

Sit in Easy Pose with a straight spine.

MUDRA: Put the fingertip of the Mercury (pinkie) finger under the thumb tip to form Buddhi Mudra. The elbows are straight, with hands extended over knees. Palms face forward.

EYES: Focus at the tip of the nose or 1/10th open.

MANTRA: Chant this mantra. *(You can use a recording, like that by Guru-shabd Singh.)*

> **Saa ray saa saa,**
> **Saa ray saa saa,**
> **Saa ray saa saa, saa rang**
> **Har ray har har,**
> **Har ray har har,**
> **Har ray har har, har rang**

Saa is the totality of God.
Har is the Earth and creative manifestation of God.
Ray is the pure power and spirit.

TIME: **31 minutes**.

Antar Naad Meditation

COMMENTS

This meditation is to develop automatic dialogue between the chakras—the one you project from and the one you project to. The essence of communication is an effort to create a common notion and a commitment from that to actions. You need flexibility to project from one chakra to the appropriate chakra in the other person. That projection and flexibility is more important than the content itself.

This mantra combines the Heavens and the Earth, the balance of the *tattvas* so that you can have power in each word. Your words will have impact and create a dialogue through the chakras. Since all of life is a creative dialogue with the psyche, if you master this meditation, you can automatically use the wisdom of the past, present and future. All knowledge of the three worlds and the totality will come through that person who masters the recitation of this mantra. This mantra is the base of all mantras. It gives you the capacity of effective communication so your words have mastery and impact.

That is the power of the Shabd Guru. The quantum process of the Shabd Guru guides and integrates experience into a higher, refined level for profound learning and practical use. It preserves balance and a sense of higher identity amidst the flood of information and change we must handle in the Aquarian Age. We must sophisticatedly educate that inner sense of the self so we can have a foundation in the self upon which to accurately weigh the deluge of information. This will only be possible by learning and teaching the quantum technology of the Shabd Guru as part of any complete education curriculum.

The quantum process of the Shabd Guru sets the brain to a new level of functioning. It gives the mind the caliber and strength to process any range of information. Teaching the quantum technology of the Shabd Guru as a core part of an Aquarian curriculum will become commonplace in the future. Real education for the Aquarian Age blends devotion with discipline, intelligence with intuition, and understanding with the capacity to act and project with integrity. It will be perceived not as a philosophy or a set of values. It will be seen as part of the training of the experience of self, so that you can embody your philosophy, carry your values, increase your spiritual fitness and deliver your self as an answer to the challenge and imperative of the Age.

Meditation to Listen to the Intuititve Sounds Around Us

Sit straight, with a very straight spine.

PART ONE

MUDRA: Bend the elbows and stretch them out to the sides of the body, up at the shoulder level. Bring the forearms near the chest, and interlock the fingers in Venus Lock—for women, left thumb and right little finger on the outside; for men, right thumb, left little finger on the outside. Place the Venus Lock palms facing the body, about 6-8 inches away from the chin. This angle has to be properly maintained to be able to do the breath properly, and get the correct result. Hold the posture steady.

EYES: Look at the tip of the nose.

BREATH: Inhale long and deep, and expand the chest and ribs by keeping the grip of the hands and pulling powerfully. As you exhale, relax it.

TIME: Continue for **14 minutes**.

TO END: Immediately move into Part Two, with no break.

PART TWO

MUDRA: Place the hands in the lap, maintaining Venus Lock as in Part I.

BREATH: Breathe very long and deep.

FOCUS: Try to become thoughtless. Have no thoughts. Become still and silent. Feel and hear everything. Sit silently for **1 minute**.

MANTRA: Play *Ong Namo, Guru Dev Namo* (recording by Nirinjan Kaur played in class.)
Play it a high sound level* for **2 minutes**.
Then play *Guru Dev Mata, Guru Dev Pita* (recording by Guru Jiwan Singh played in class). Listen to the recording for **4 minutes**, then begin singing the words aloud, copying the sound exactly. Try to catch the sound and the projection of it, whether or not you have learned the words and translations.

TIME: Continue for **11-31 minutes**. (Done for 20 minutes when taught.)

TO END: Inhale deeply as you stretch upward. Then relax.

You will find the mantra Guru Dev Mata by Guru Arjan Dev in the Appendix.

* *Use your common sense based on your sound system.*

The Divine Shield Meditation for Protection & Positivity

SITTING POSITION: Raise the right knee up with the right foot flat on the ground, toes pointing straight ahead. Place the sole of the left foot against the arch and ankle of the right foot. The ball of the left foot rests just in front of the ankle bone of the right foot.

MUDRA: Make a fist of the left hand and place it on the ground beside the hip. Use this to balance the posture. Bend the right elbow and place it on the top of the right knee. Bring the right hand back along the side of the head with the palm facing the ear. Form a shallow cup of the right palm. Then bring it against the skull so that it contacts the skull below the ear but stays open above the ear. It is as if you formed a cup of the hand to amplify a faint sound that you want to hear.

EYE: The eyes are closed and focused at the Brow Point.

MANTRA: Inhale deeply and chant the mantra in a long, full, smooth sound. Project the sound as if someone is listening to you. As you chant, listen to the sound and let it vibrate through your whole body. If you chant in a group, hear the overtones that develop and let those tones vibrate all around you and in every cell of your body. The mantra is:

Maaaaaaaaaaaaaaaaaa

Chant it at a comfortable high pitch. When you have exhaled completely, take another deep breath and continue. In a group you may all inhale at different times. The group sound will seem continuous.

TIME: Continue for **11-31 minutes**. Then change sides. Continue for an equal amount of time. Start slowly. Learn to hold the concentration into the sound. Build the meditation on each side to a total of **62 minutes**.

TO END: At the end of this second meditation sit still for a few minutes. Let your mind be aware, still, open and innocent.

COMMENTS
Chant as if you are a child calling upon the Divine Mother for Protection.

Butterfly Kriya

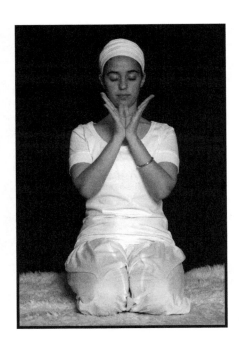

Sit on the heels in Rock Pose.

MUDRA: Bring the heels of your hands together in front of the throat—making a V with your hands. The four fingers are together and the thumbs are touching and stretched back toward the body.

EYES: Focus the eyes at the tip of the nose.

MOVEMENT: From this V, begin rhythmically clapping the hands. The movement is like a hinge or a butterfly. Keep the thumbs together and the heels of the hands together as you open and close the hand. Make it a steady movement, not too fast, not too slow.

TIME: **11 to 62 minutes.**

COMMENTS

It will create the sound, Har, Har, if you really do it right. That's where the sound Har came from. Har, Har —if you accurately take pavan, the air, it will create the sound, Har. It's a natural thing. Mentally the sound is Har, physically the sound is Har. Concentrate. —Yogi Bhajan

Meditation for Conscious Communication to Experience the Naad

Sit straight in Easy Pose.

PART ONE

EYES: Eyes look down, focusing clearly on each word without having to move the paper, creating a light Neck Lock. Peripheral vision will catch the outline of the nose. Fix the optical nerve to make the pituitary become focused and directive, not negative or reactive. This is the first principle for success in this meditation. Fix the eyes.

MANTRA: *Say Saraswati.* Hold the mantra sheet in the right hand. These are Yogi Bhajan's words put to music by Nirinjan Kaur Khalsa under his supervision.

MUDRA: Hold the paper in front of you, as if you are holding a sheet of music. Do not lean in your posture or move. Sit comfortably, and pick the angle of your arm that lets you detect the outline of the nose as you focus clearly on each word you recite.

TIME: **23 minutes**.

PART TWO

MUDRA: Press the hands on the Heart Center, left palm on the heart, right palm resting on the left hand, eyes tightly closed. Chant for **8 minutes**.

TO END: Inhale deeply. Hold the breath for 20 seconds, pull in the navel and concentrate. Exhale. Repeat for 20 seconds, then 30 seconds.

Say Saraswatee Sar-rang
Hay Bhagvatee Har-rang
La Lakhshmee Nar-ring
Karn Kar-an Kar-ring
Dayv Maa-haa Dayv Dayv-uh
Sarab Shaktee Seva
Tarn Taran Tar-ring
Neel Narayan Nar-ring
Guroo Dayv Dayv-ing
Sarab Lok Sev-ing

Goddess of Love — Happiness
Shakti Power — Victory
Goddess of Wealth — Prosperity
God's Three Aspects — Fulfillment
Nurtures the Experience of Totality
The God of Gods, the Infinite One
Under and Over, God Is Love
All Creation, Serving

COMMENTS

This meditation uses the *Say Saraswati* mantra to invoke the power of the *Naad* to lock the brain and mind into a new pattern. The posture used demonstrates a technique of meditation reflecting many ancient practices where people would read sacred texts in a manner that assured deep transformation. We look at the tip of the nose because it captures the function of the pituitary so that we do not simply react to each wandering thought and feeling. If the pituitary is off, not locked in with you, then two thirds of the time your mind will wander. The moment the optical nerve is locked on anything within the sight of the nose, you are in control.

These affirmations are Yogi Bhajan's: "Their permutation and combination is according to meridian points in the upper palate which stimulates the hypothalamus. The hypothalamus will react and act with the glandular system and move the pituitary from the inside naturally, not from the outside. Therefore there is no breathing involved with it. The moment the pituitary is forced to take a certain movement of its own secretion, it will affect the glandular system. It will change the radiation cycle of the pineal, the little medical stone in the brain. This is the science of the *Naad*, and you will experience it."

Both the English and Sanskrit sounds used in this mantra are true to the *Naad*. If you simply do it the result will be definite. You will find the next day that your way of speaking has changed.

Healing the Wounds of Love
Mera Man Lochai Gur Darshan Taa-ee

Sit in Easy Pose with a straight spine, and a light Neck Lock.

MANTRA: The first four stanzas of Shabd Hazaray, which are the letters written by Guru Arjan Dev to Guru Ram Das.

There are four verses that make up this section of Shabd Hazaray. To that sound current we interweave the mantra:

Aad sach, jugaad sach,

Haibhay sach, naanak hosee bhai sach

True in the beginning, True throughout the Ages
True at this moment, Nanak says this Truth shall ever be.

The sequence of chanting will be:
Aad Sach Mantra *(one time)*
First Letter
Aad Sach Mantra *(one time)*
Second Letter
Aad Sach Mantra *(one time)*
Third Letter
Aad Sach Mantra *(one time)*
Fourth Letter
Aad Sach Mantra *(four times)*

See page 108 for practice of this Meditation as a powerful group experience.
Healing the Wound of Love recording by Guru Raj Kaur was created for this Meditation.

COMMENTS
If you want to change your relationships, drop the pain, empower them with clarity, sensitivity and authenticity, do this meditation **11 times once a day for 11 days**. You can do it each day for as long as you feel necessary or as long as you are enthralled with the beauty and space it creates.

These verses create sound as mantras written in the form of letters between Guru Arjan, the fifth Guru, and Guru Ram Das, his father, the fourth Guru. There was perfect longing, love and fulfillment in the sentiments, feelings, projection and elevation of these letters. Repeating these mantras takes us out of the normal internal chatter and emotional games of the mind we usually live with. It purifies, aligns and strengthens the heart and soul.

GURU ARJAN DEV, SIRI GURU GRANTH SAHIB
My mind longs for a sight of my Guru.
It cries out like the thirsty chatrik bird waiting for the rain.
But the rain does not come.
Peace does not come without the sight of my beloved Guru.
I am a sacrifice, my soul is a sacrifice,
Unto the sight of my Beloved Guru. (1)

Your face is so beautiful; hearing your Word brings me deep peace.
It has been so long since this chatrik has seen any water.
O, my dearest friend, O my beloved Guru.
Blessed is the ground beneath your feet.
I am a sacrifice, I am ever a sacrifice
Unto my dearest friend and intimate, my beloved Guru. (2)

Every moment I am away from you a Dark Age dawns for me.
When will I see you, O my beloved Master?
I cannot get through the night without the sight of your Court.
Sleep does not come.
I am a sacrifice, my soul is a sacrifice
Unto the Court of my True Guru. (3)

I am blessed, for I am with my Saintly Guru.
I have found the Eternal God within my own heart/home.
I will serve you every moment of my life, and never be separate from you again. I am a sacrifice, my soul is a sacrifice unto you.
O my Master, Slave Nanak lives to serve you. (4)

Healing the Wounds of Love
Mera Man Lochai Gur Darshan Taa-ee
The Four Letters of Guru Arjan to Guru Ram Das
from Shabd Hazaray Guru Arjan Dev, Siri Guru Granth Sahib, page 96

Aad sach, jugaad such, haibhai sach,
naanak hosee bhai sach

FIRST
Mayraa man lochai gur darshan taa-ee
Bilap karay chaatrik kee ni-aa-ee
Trikhaa na utarai shaant na aavai
Bin Darshan Sant pi-aaray jee-o
Hao gholee jee-o ghol ghumaa-ee
Gur darshan sant pi-aaray jee-o (1)

Aad sach, jugaad sach, haibhai sach,
naanak hosee bhai sach

SECOND
Tayraa mukh suhaavaa jee-o sahaj dhun baanee
Chir ho-aa daykhay saaring paanee
Dhan so days jahaa too(n) vasi-aa
Mayray sajan meet muraaray jee-o
Hao gholee hao ghol ghumaa-ee
Gur sajan meet muraaray jee-o (2)

Aad sach, jugaad sach, haibhai sach,
naanak hosee bhai sach

THIRD
Ik gharee na milatay taa kalijug hotaa
Hun kad milee-ai pri-a tudh bhagavantaa
Mo-eh rain na vihaavai need na aavai
Bin daykhay gur darbaaray jee-o
Hao gholee jee-o ghol ghumaa-ee
Tis sachay gur darbaaray jee-o (3)

Aad sach, jugaad sach, haibhai sach,
naanak hosee bhai sach

FOURTH
Bhaag ho-aa gur sant milaa-i-aa
Prabh abinaasee ghar meh paa-i-aa
Sayv karee pal chasaa na vichhuraa
Jan Naanak daas tumaaray jee-o
Hao gholee jee-o ghol ghumaa-ee
Jan Naanak daas tumaaray jee-o (4)

Aad sach, jugaad sach, haibhai sach, naanak hosee bhai sach
Aad sach, jugaad sach, haibhai sach, naanak hosee bhai sach
Aad sach, jugaad sach, haibhai sach, naanak hosee bhai sach
Aad sach, jugaad sach, haibhai sach, naanak hosee bhai sach

THIS IS HOW THE SHABD APPEARS ON PAGE 96 OF SIRI GURU GRANTH SAHIB.
IT IS IN RAAG MAAJ, THE BANI OF GURU ARJAN.

ਮੇਰਾ ਮਨ ਲੋਚੈ ਗੁਰ ਦਰਸਨ ਤਾਈ
ਬਲਪ ਕਰੇ ਚਾਤ੍ਰਿਕ ਕੀ ਨਿਆਈ
ਤ੍ਰਿਖਾ ਨ ਉਤਰੈ ਸਾਂਤਿ ਨ ਆਵੈ
ਬਿਨੁ ਦਰਸਨ ਸੰਤ ਪਿਆਰੇ ਜੀਉ ॥੧॥
ਹਉ ਘੋਲੀ ਜੀਉ ਘੋਲਿ ਘੁਮਾਈ
ਗੁਰ ਦਰਸਨ ਸੰਤ ਪਿਆਰੇ ਜੀਉ ॥੧॥

ਤੇਰਾ ਮੁਖ ਸੁਹਾਵਾ ਜੀਉ ਸਹਜ ਧੁਨਿ ਬਾਨੀ
ਚਿਰੁ ਹੋਆ ਦੇਖੇ ਸਾਰਿੰਗਪਾਨੀ
ਧੰਨੁ ਸੁ ਦੇਸੁ ਜਹਾ ਤੂੰ ਵਸਿਆ
ਮੇਰੇ ਸਜਣ ਮੀਤ ਮੁਰਾਰੇ ਜੀਉ ॥੨॥
ਹਉ ਘੋਲੀ ਹਉ ਘੋਲਿ ਘੁਮਾਈ
ਗੁਰ ਸਜਣ ਮੀਤ ਮੁਰਾਰੇ ਜੀਉ ॥੧॥

ਇਕ ਘੜੀ ਨ ਮਿਲਤੇ ਤਾ ਕਲਿਜੁਗੁ ਹੋਤਾ
ਹੁਨਿ ਕਦਿ ਮਿਲੀਐ ਪ੍ਰਿਅ ਤੁਧੁ ਭਗਵੰਤਾ
ਮੋਹਿ ਰੈਨਿ ਨ ਵਿਹਾਵੈ ਨੀਦ ਨ ਆਵੈ
ਬਿਨੁ ਦੇਖੇ ਗੁਰ ਦਰਬਾਰੇ ਜੀਉ ॥੩॥

ਹਉ ਘੋਲੀ ਜੀਉ ਘੋਲਿ ਘੁਮਾਈ
ਤਿਸੁ ਸਚੇ ਗੁਰ ਦਰਬਾਰੇ ਜੀਉ ॥੧॥
ਭਾਗੁ ਹੋਆ ਗੁਰਿ ਸੰਤ ਮਿਲਾਇਆ
ਪ੍ਰਭ ਅਬਿਨਾਸੀ ਘਰ ਮਹਿ ਪਾਇਆ
ਸੇਵ ਕਰੀ ਪਲ ਚਸਾ ਨ ਵਿਛੁੜਾ
ਜਨ ਨਾਨਕ ਦਾਸ ਤੁਮਾਰੇ ਜੀਉ ॥੪॥
ਹਉ ਘੋਲੀ ਜੀਉ ਘੋਲਿ ਘੁਮਾਈ
ਜਨ ਨਾਨਕ ਦਾਸ ਤੁਮਾਰੇ ਜੀਉ ॥੧॥੮॥

Removing Fear of the Future

Sit comfortably in Easy Pose.

MUDRA: Begin by resting the back of the left hand in the palm of the right hand. Grab the left hand with the right, so that the right thumb nestles in the left palm. Cross the left thumb over the right. The fingers of the right hand curve around the outside of the left hand and hold it gently. Holding your hands in this way will give you a peaceful, secure feeling.

Place this mudra at the Heart Center, resting against the chest.

MANTRA: Meditate to your favorite version of the shabd:
Dhan Dhan Ram Das Gur.
(The words and meaning of this shabd can be found in the Appendix.)

TIME: Start with **11 minutes** and gradually work up to **31 minutes** of practice.

TO END: Inhale deeply and relax.

COMMENTS

This meditation clears the fear of the future which has been created by your subconscious memories of the past. It connects you to the flow of life through your Heart Center.

"The beauty in you is your spirit. The strength in you is your endurance. The intelligence in you is your vastness." — Yogi Bhajan

"The crossed thumbs help neutralize your mind's frantic calculations to avoid fear and pain. It is the calculations themselves that produce anxiety and get you out of touch with the resources of your intuition and heart." — Gurucharan Singh Khalsa, Director of Training

CHAPTER FOUR

OPENING THE HEART & RESTORING THE LOVE

SERVING THE INFINITE

Love is Love

If you want to play the game of love, put your head on the
palm of your hand and walk this path with me.
—Guru Gobind Singh, Tenth Master of the Sikhs

Transformation in the game of love requires a complete reorientation to the rules of the game. In order to truly experience love, and union, we must begin by playing with a new rule book. In the West, we have been trained to look for that one person—our soul mate—who can fulfill our longing, who can give us what we believe we need or want from a relationship. To truly love, we must first fulfill that longing within ourselves, with the Infinite, the love of God. Anything less will fall short. No human being can fill that particular hole—not even a soul mate. Then, from that fullness of love, that union within ourselves, we can begin to love whoever comes across our path. We can serve with equanimity all who come to seek solace, healing or forgiveness. We can love the enemy and the friend. We have the capacity to sacrifice for others without losing ourselves—because we've already given our head. We've already surrendered our will to the Will of the Infinite. We live in the flow of love.

"It's not a big offering at all, don't hesitate. These things look very ridiculous to some of us because we are a very egocentric, concentrated and saturated society, but you must understand, this is the greatest beauty of Nature, nothing happens without two. Nothing. If the rose wants to spread its fragrance, it needs air. If water wants to become cloud, it needs sun. Every action in the state of mono-existence creates nothing, nothing can happen; action requires two to produce something, positive or negative."[1]

– Yogi Bhajan

How do we break out of our egocentric orientation and truly allow the other to come in so that our creativity can flower, so that our action and efforts can be fruitful and productive? How do we learn to co-operate? First, we have to be open to receiving the other; so, how exactly do we open our hearts? Kriya to Open the Heart Center and the Meditation to Open the Lock of the Heart are excellent ways to begin this lifelong process. It takes courage and effort to open the heart. Be brave! For the open heart is a liberated heart. The open heart is boundless, without limitation or fear. The open heart loves, spontaneously.

Once our hearts our open, our own experience of Infinity, our own inner union flowers and bears the fruit of love: compassion. The kriyas in this chapter cultivate the capacity for inner union so that we are complete and whole. Once our own inner integrity is established, we can enter into relationships with others with something to give—not looking for something to take. From this inner balance we can then find balance with the other—so that the two can become one once again.

Love is Love. There's no condition. There's no lack. There's nothing to find and there's certainly nothing to take. Love can only be received—and given—from the fullness of the liberated heart. Free yourself from ego, give your head, so that you can know love and share that love with all.

1 The Teachings of Yogi Bhajan, March 1, 1973

Kriya to Open the Heart Center

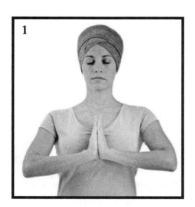

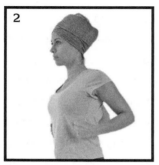

1. Stand with palms together in Prayer Pose at the center of the chest and do a steady Breath of Fire. **3 minutes**. Inhale and hold briefly at the end.

2. Stand or sit with an erect spine. Keep the eyes open and look to the horizon. Make fists of both hands. Begin alternately punching with one fist then the other. Together the hands create a piston-like motion with one arm pulling back to balance the other arm punching forward. The hands do not turn or twist. Exhale with each punch forward and punch rapidly so the breath becomes like a Breath of Fire. Continue for **3 minutes**.

TO END: inhale, draw both elbows back, tighten the fists, apply root lock, and suspend the breath for 5 seconds. Exhale and relax.

3. Stand straight, extend the arms out to the sides, and begin to make big circles with both arms at the same time. Inhale as they come forward and up, and exhale as they go back and down. Continue for **2 minutes**.

TO END: Inhale and stretch both arms straight up over the head. Exhale and relax.

4. Sit straight. Interlace the fingers with the thumbtips touching.
   a) Position the hands 4-6 inches in front of the chest with both palms facing down. Lift the elbows to the same level.
   b) Inhale as you lift the hands up to the level of the throat.
   c) Exhale as you sweep them down to the level of the Navel.
Create a steady pumping motion with a powerful breath, and continue for **3 minutes**.

TO END: inhale, bring the hands to the level of the heart, and suspend the breath for 10 seconds. Exhale and relax.

Kriya to Open the Heart Center

5. Stand or sit with a straight spine. Place the hands beside the shoulders with elbows by your sides and palms facing forward. Close your eyelids halfway and fix your gaze downward. Begin to slowly inhale and exhale. Your breath should be equal on the inhale and the exhale. Mentally repeat the following primal sound scale on both the inhale and exhale:

Saa Taa Naa Maa

Press the thumb tips to the finger tips sequentially from the first finger tip to the little finger tip with *Saa Taa Naa Maa*, while you vibrate the mental sounds, as you would with Kirtan Kriya. Continue for **3-5 minutes**.

6. Sit with a straight spine. Block the right nostril gently with the index finger of the right hand. Inhale slowly through your left nostril, exhale slowly through rounded lips. Match the duration of the inhale and exhale, with each one lasting about 10 seconds. Continue with this slow breathing pattern for **3 minutes**. Then relax and follow the natural flow of your breath for another **2 minutes**.

COMMENTS

This is an intermediate level set to create open loving feelings. It opens the heart, increases compassion and sensitivity to others, and helps you to drop emotional defensiveness. Its calming effect allows you to eliminate unnecessary thoughts and feelings, so you can be more in the present and experience your feelings more clearly.

Polarity Balance Kriya

1. Begin standing up. Balance on the right foot. Extend and stretch the right arm forward and up parallel to the ground, palm down. Left foot is lifted back and up 45 degrees and extended straight. Extend through the core of the body. Hold steady **2 minutes**. Then switch arms and legs and repeat for **2 minutes**. *Balance is the basis of health.*

2. Stand straight. Spread legs as wide as possible. Extend arms straight out, parallel to ground, palms down, wrists straight. Squat down so legs form 60-degree angle, about 1/4 way down. Inhale up, exhale down. Continue for **5 minutes**.
This will put pressure on the hips, spine and the muscles along the back.

3. Keep standing and begin to march in place. Move the arms back and forth with a precise and controlled movement. The left arm should move forward as the right knee comes up. Continue alternating sides. For the final minute, increase the pace, moving powerfully. **5 minutes**.

4. Spread the legs as wide as possible. Place hands, fingers interlaced, behind the neck. Begin to rotate hips in wide circles. The knees stay straight. Allow the entire body to move and rotate. Continue for **3 minutes**.

Polarity Balance Kriya

5. Place hands on hips. March by lifting heels and bend knees but keep toes on the ground. Dance on the toes. The hips will move. The calves will receive a pressure. Continue for **3 minutes**.

6. Begin "Jumping Jacks." Hands come together over head as legs spread. Arms down by sides as legs come together. Jump in a rhythm. Continue for **3 minutes**.

7. Still standing, lift alternate arms and legs. Right arm extends up as the left heel lifts up to strike the buttocks. Switch arm and leg. **3 minutes**.

8. Face a partner. Do exercise #7, but grasp hands, and lift legs together on alternate sides as legs go back. **1 1/2 minutes**.

Continued on the next page.

Polarity Balance Kriya

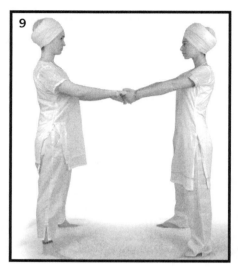

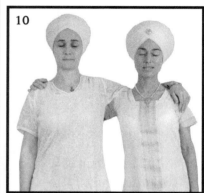

9. Stay with partner. Spread legs. Hold hands facing each other. Squat in deep knee bend, then come up. Inhale up, exhale down. Continue for **3 minutes**.

10. Stand up. Be arm and arm with each other in straight lines. Close your eyes and stand still. Chant with the *Bountiful, Blissful and Beautiful* recording. Continue for **6 minutes**.

11. Sit in Easy Pose. Fold hands at the Heart Center in Prayer Pose. Listen to the same recording. Meditate at the Brow Point. **5 minutes**. Relax.

12. Turn to a person next to you and lock hands and wrestle. **30 seconds**.

Meditation to Open the Lock of the Heart

Sit in Easy Pose with a straight spine.

MUDRA: Bring hands approximately 6-8 inches in front of your face, palms flat and facing one another, fingers pointing toward the ceiling. Have palms approximately 6-8 inches between. Elbows are bent and are relaxed down.

MOVEMENT: With a very fast, powerful jerk, stretch the hands out, until there is about 36 inches between the hands, and abruptly stop them there. The stopping process will be so abrupt, done with such a powerful force, that you'll find the hands, chest, shoulders, and head jerking back and forth a little bit. This abrupt stopping, and the resulting jerk causes an "opening up your chest cavity with a 'current shock.' You should stretch out like eleven hundred volts have hit you."

MANTRA: Listen to the recording *Tantric Har*, or 1 movement per second. Do not sing aloud. On every *Har*, you will stretch your arms with a powerful force. Concentrate on this reaction in your chest, and see the effect it has on you.

EYES: Unspecified.

TIME: **11 minutes**.

TO END: Inhale. Hold the breath, but keep on doing the motion. Hold 13 seconds. Exhale. Inhale again and continue the motion. Hold 8 seconds. Exhale. Inhale deeply, continue. Hold 6 seconds. Relax.

COMMENTS

The chest cavity is called the Heart Chakra. This heavy jolt, as you spring your hands and arms apart, will cause a jerking reaction to your chest cavity, which will open up your Heart Center. Opening of your Heart Center cavity is opening up to your own Infinity.

This center is sometimes referred to as the *agan granthi*—the place from which all fire-related activites spring—food, digestion, breath, to name a few. When this center is locked, your rib cage is out of place. Then the diaphragm doesn't act right, and you'll lose one third of your life force. This meditation loosens this lock and will open up the power of the Almighty within you.

You must bring forth the entire power of your being, using a great force as you open up and then suddenly stop your arms, and thus shock your central nervous system (the *sushmuna*) on the sound of *Har*. Through this meditation you can move the power of the *ida* and *pingala*, and open up the *sushmuna*.

How Much You Love

PART ONE

A Male and Female Balance of Creativity

MUDRA: The left arm is bent, palm flat, facing out like a pledge at the shoulder level (below the eyebrow). The right palm is also flat and facing out. The bottom of the right wrist should be slightly above and parallel to the eyebrows. The right forearm angles in toward the face. The right hand is up and the left hand is low.

EYES: Look at the tip of the nose.

BREATH: Breath slowly.

MUSIC: *Every Heartbeat* by Nirinjan Kaur.

TIME: **15 minutes**. The first 2 minutes are done in silence.

TO END: Inhale and suspend the breath for 10 seconds while stretching the arms straight up. Exhale and relax for **3 minutes**.

This is a powerful exercise to make you young. This is the best gift you can give to your physical body.

PART TWO

Sit Straight. Elbows are wide and bent so the forearms are parallel to the ground and slightly wider than the hips. Palms are face down, fingers spread wide, open and tight. Bounce the hands in an alternate motion, as if you are playing ball. The motion should be very fast; the body will jerk.

EYES: Eyes are closed. Look up to the center of the skull.

TIME: **8 minutes**; the final 2 minutes should be done very fast and very powerfully.

TO END: Inhale, synchronize your body. Tighten all the muscles of your body. Exhale. Repeat 2 times. Relax for 3 minutes.

You can avoid disease. Just remember this exercise.

How Much You Love

PART THREE

Come into Baby Pose. Sitting on the heels, put the forehead to the ground. The arms are resting on the ground behind you with the palms facing up.

MUSIC: Play something pretty, relaxing, and uplifting.

TIME: **4 minutes**. Use the final minute to slowly, slowly rise back up.

PART FOUR
The Prayer

Sit straight and reach up. Arms are at a 60-degree angle and slightly in front of the body. Stretch out from the shoulders, stretch the arms very straight, with no bend in the elbows. Palms are flat, facing each other.

EYES: Look toward the sky, the heavens, then close the eyes.

TIME: **2 minutes**

Pray. Trust in your prayer. Ask and it shall be fulfilled. Open your heart. Dwell in God. It will bring all happiness and bliss.

COMMENTS
"Love confronts. Love has no fear. . . . Love is the ultimate power. It knows no defeat. It doesn't know impossible. It's a strength, it's not a weakness. There's a tremendous amount of pain in love. That's realism. But do the lovers feel it? No. There's a joy. In history, you will find people in love of God tortured in many ways. They smiled. They laughed. Where did their strength come from? It was their love. I would like to let you know how much you love. Let's measure it by a straight balance of frequency. You will know it."

—Yogi Bhajan

Reverse Adi Shakti Kriya

PART ONE

Bring the right hand 6 to 9 inches above the crown of the head, like you are blessing yourself. The left hand is by the shoulder, palm facing forward, like a pledge—like you are blessing the Universe.

BREATH: Breathe long, slow and deep. Build up to a One Minute Breath. Kiss the breath, with affection and feeling, "a hug kind of feeling." Breathe consciously. If you are doing it correctly, the taste in your mouth will change.

EYES: The eyes are closed. Roll the eyes down and look at the chin. Keep this eye position throughout the three parts.

Bless you, bless your ancestors and those who will come after you. This blessing is not a social phenomenon. You are mentally, hypnotically blessing you. It will affect the magnetic field and it will hurt you if you are an angry person. Keep breathing consciously. If you cannot bless yourself, nobody can. Better you bless yourself; heavens will bless you. After 5 minutes, it should start to hurt and let you know what you have been eating. When you have pain, the brain will produce natural morphine. If these ducts are open, endurance will develop, physically, emotionally and spiritually.

TIME: **11 minutes**.
TO END: Inhale and transition into the second position.

PART TWO

Extend the arms straight out, parallel to the ground, with the palms facing down. Straighten the arms tight and stretch.

TIME: **3 minutes**.
TO END: Inhale deep and raise arms into the third position.
This will strengthen the heart and open the heart center.

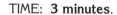

PART THREE

Raise the arms straight up and stretch. Palms are flat and face forward.
Do not bend the elbows.
TIME: **3 minutes**.
TO END: Inhale deep and hold tight for 15 seconds. Stretch. Lift the spine.
Exhale with Cannon Breath. Repeat 3 times.

Can you spare seventeen minutes for yourself in twenty-four hours? This meditation will totally change you from the inside out. It will give you self-consciousness, self-experience, self-love and then, you can love everybody. Become total.

Compassion Kriya

Sit in Easy Pose with the spine straight.

MUDRA: Cross the Saturn (middle) fingers over the Jupiter (index) fingers of each hand. Place thumbs on mounds of Mercury, which are just at the base of the Mercury (pinkie) fingers.

EYES: Eyes are closed.

MANTRA: Sing with a lyrical version of *Rakhay Rakhanahaar.*

MOVEMENT:
a) On the first line of the mantra, bring the hands up and press them into the chest, right palm over the left.

b) On the second line of the mantra, lower the arms so wrists rest on knees. Continue alternating in this way, but with the hands at the chest for the last line that repeats twice. Then briefly lower and raise again for the first line.

> a) *Rakhay rakhanhaar aap ubaariun*
> b) *Gur kee pairee paa-eh kaaj savaariun*
> a) *Hoaa aap dayaal manho na visaariun*
> b) *Saadh janaa kai sung bhavjal taariun*
> a) *Saakat nindak dusht khin maa-eh bidaariun*
> b) *Tis Saahib kee tayk naanak manai maa-eh*
> a) *Jis simrat sukh ho-eh saglay dookh jaa-eh*
> a) *Jis simrat sukh ho-eh saglay dookh jaa-eh*

(Briefly lower the hands and then continue.)

TIME: **31 minutes**.

COMMENTS
The only beautiful thing which makes you human is compassion. Think about vengeance, lies, truth, God, greatness, think of anything, if you take compassion out of it, everything becomes bitter. Compassion is a value of life; it is power; it is God and meditation; it is truth. Compassion gives you the strength to go through suffering and yet, feel no pain. There is absolutely no grace without compassion.

Merger of the Sun & Moon

Sit in a comfortable meditative posture. Chin in and chest out.

MUDRA: Bring the elbows in to the sides of the body and bring the hands palm up, fingers together, with the wrists bent back and the fingertips facing out to each side, parallel with the shoulders. Take care to maintain the hand position throughout the exercise.

EYES: Eyes focused at the tip of the nose. As you continue the meditation, the eyes should relax and may roll up.

BREATH & MOVEMENT:
1. Inhale and lift the left hand and shoulder up toward the ear, keeping the hand bent back and parallel to the floor. As you inhale, you will feel that the left nostril is more active than the right.
    Exhale through the left nostril and lower the hand, returning to the original position. Repeat on opposite side.

2. Inhale and lift the right hand and shoulders up. As you inhale you will feel that the right nostril is more active.
    Exhale through the right nostril and lower the hand, returning to the original position.

Continue to alternate sides and alternate nostrils, with a steady, evenly paced breath, not too fast, and not too slow. This movement serves to open the nostril on the same side, so that as you move alternate hands, the breath will also alternate from side to side.

TIME: **11 minutes**. Can be increased with practice and experience.

TO END: Inhale and stretch the arms up, looking through the 10th Gate (the Crown Chakra at the top of the head). Exhale and relax.

Venus Kriya

Sit facing a partner with knees touching, looking into his or her eyes.

MUDRA: Put the palms together with your partner's.

MANTRA: Begin chanting the Maha Shakti mantra, moving the hands alternatively toward the partner.
   The woman chants the first word, the man the second and so on.

**Gobinday, Mukanday, Udaaray, Apaaray,
Hareeang, Kareeang, Nirnaamay, Akaamay**

These are the eight aspects of God:
   *Sustainer, Liberator, Enlightener, Infinite,
   Destroyer, Creator, Nameless, Desireless.*

TIME: **3 minutes**.

COMMENTS

Venus Kriyas are Kundalini Yoga exercises done with a partner, usually a partner of the opposite sex. Although Venus Kriyas are less intense than White Tantric Yoga, they intensify the experience of the exercise through the polarities of the male-female interaction. In Venus Kriyas, the energetic and sensory connections of the partners are used to elevate sexual and sensory energy to a connection based on awareness and the capacity to see the sacred in the other.

   Do not line up in lines as in White Tantric Yoga. Two people can sit together anywhere. If you line up, then the energy is shared diagonally. That is not the intention of a Venus Kriya.

Love is Love

Sit in an easy cross-legged position, or sit in a chair with a straight spine and both feet flat on the floor.

MUDRA: Place your hands in Gyan Mudra, thumb and index finger touching each other with the other fingers straight. With the hands in this position, cross the right hand over the left at the Heart Center, but not touching the chest. The right palm is against the back of the left hand.

EYES: Eyes are closed.

MANTRA: Repeat the affirmation with Yogi Bhajan using the *Destiny* CD from Kundalini Research Institute.

Love is Love

TIME: **11-31 minutes.**

TO END: Inhale, suspend the breath. Exhale, release the mudra. Relax.

CHAPTER FIVE

COMMUNICATION:
SPEAKING &
LISTENING

SERVING THE INFINITE

Conscious Communication

"The idea, the purpose of life, is to transform your consciousness into the consciousness of another person and understand on a mutual ground, so that there can be peace."[1]

–Yogi Bhajan

We all want to communicate. In fact, we need to communicate. We want to express ourselves. We want to be known. But to truly communicate, we have to be ready and able to listen as well as to speak. In a world of chatting, texting and twitter, we've lost the art of listening. It's one-sided with only the illusion of interface, intercommunication. As a collective culture, we're not listening; so there can be no dialogue—only monologue.

We communicate for many reasons. We want to persuade others, to tell our side of the story, to relay information that we think is important. Our entire focus is on what we're going to say. How many times have we found ourselves just planning what we're going to say next? On the other hand, how often have we entered into a communication with the intention to listen to what the other person has to say? How often have we relaxed and opened ourselves up to curiosity about the other? Our culture has grown so narcissistic that many of us have lost the ability to listen, openly and honestly, to another person. Instead we just batter one another with information. Information isn't communication.

Communication is a relay between two parties who have a common purpose. The key word is common—communion—or as Yogi Bhajan often put it, "a com-

mon notion." Communication implies a kind of fellowship among those who seek common ground. All too often we witness an entirely different kind of communication, one that has nothing to do with finding communion. Instead, it's aggressive or persuasive or manipulative or condescending. It's all about establishing hierarchies of power, rather than generating mutually beneficial outcomes. The first step is to seek and find understanding—mutual understanding—which takes listening skills. Learning to listen in this way is an application of what we know about *Naad*—listening for the rhythm, the pattern, and the intention behind the sounds. Listening in this way requires subtlety and patience. It requires us to listen to the sound within the sound and actually hear what the person means, not just what they say.

The second step is to empower our own speaking skills. Experiencing the connection between the tongue and the navel is crucial in developing this desired skill. There must be an absolute and precise relationship between the tip of the tongue and the movement of the navel. Mastering this single technique will provide you with word power and will help to balance the Third and Fifth Chakras so that your communication has impact.

Conscious communication calls us to a higher standard. We are not only responsible for our own response to communication; but we're responsible for the other person's response, too. Can you communicate with such sophistication, honesty and diplomacy that the other person not only hears you, but you also arrive at the outcome you intended? This is mastery— and it takes practice and positivity.

The third step in finding a 'common notion,' is to learn to communicate positively. As teachers and practitioners, we want to uplift ourselves and others. What better way than to communicate with positiv-ity—positive plus! This doesn't imply empty affirmations or worn out aphorisms, but instead an integrated consciousness that dwells in the prosperity and flow of Infinity. When you trust the Infinite and know, from the start, that everything is True—*Sat Nam*—then you can relax and be positive and your positivity, in turn, attracts more positive flow into your life. In this way, communication becomes a pathway to peace and prosperity. Communicate consciously—and win the day!

1 ©The Teachings of Yogi Bhajan, May 17, 1992

Adjusting the Centers of Interconnection & Intercommunication

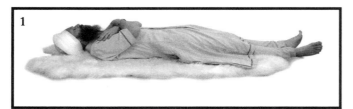

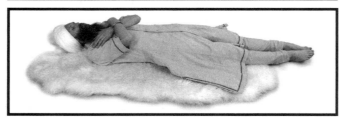

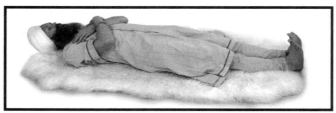

1. Lie flat on the back with the feet and legs together, crossing the wrists over your chest like a mummy. Completely relax for **1 minute**. Stay in the position, keep relaxed, and begin pointing and flexing both feet at the same time. Coordinate breath and movement. Move quickly. The breath should be heavy and loud. **4 1/2 minutes**.

If your feet and breath are not moving together, then your temples are out of position. If you feel pressure at the temples while you are doing this exercise, then slow down the movement.

2. Stay in the same mummy-like position, begin alternate leg lifts to 90 degrees. Keep legs straight with the toes pointed. Inhale up and exhale down with a loud and powerful breath. Apply upward pressure as you raise each leg. Do not apply pressure as the feet go back to the floor. Feet should silently return to the floor. **3 minutes**.

3. Still in the same mummy-like position, raise both legs to 90 degrees and lower them together. Inhale up and exhale down, moving quickly for **1 minute**. Then continue at a regular pace. **52 repetitions**.

4. Still lying on the back, firmly lock the palms over the ears and temples. Elbows point upward. Begin moving your pelvic bone and rib cage from side to side like a wriggling fish. Make this diagonal movement so heavy that you can feel it in your temples. Move the pelvic bone, rib cage, and spine. The whole torso moves. **3 1/2 minutes**.

If you move heavily and fast, it will take away the age imbalances.

Adjusting the Centers of Interconnection & Intercommunication

5. Sit on the heels, keep the spine straight, stretch the tongue out of the mouth and begin panting with a Dog Breath through the mouth, feeling the air striking the back of your throat. **1 minute**.

6. Sit on the heels, arms extended straight out with the palms facing each other. Alternately move each arm up to 45 degrees and back to the center. The left arm moves diagonally up to the right side and returns. Then the right arm moves up to the left and returns. You are drawing a big "X" in the air in front of the body. The movement is fast and powerful. The body will subtly move as the arms move. Cut the heavens. You will feel the movement in the temples and the toes if you do it strongly. **2 1/2 minutes**.

7. Still be sitting on the heels with arms by the sides with the palms facing forward. Bring the hands to the shoulders as if you are pouring water on them. Bring all five fingertips together when they touch the shoulders. Repeat the movement for **1 1/2 minutes**.
This exercise will make you feel good for the whole day.

Continued on the next page.

Adjusting the Centers of Interconnection & Intercommunication

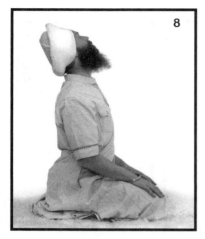

8. Still on the heels, place the hands on the thighs and begin flexing the whole body. Flex it well, lower back, middle back, upper back, and neck. **1 1/2 minutes**.

9. Sit like a Yogi and chant the following mantra in a monotone using the tip of the tongue:

Haree Har, Haree Har, Haree Har, Haree

One recitation of the mantra takes about 3 seconds.
Continue for **9 1/2 minutes**.

In class Yogi Bhajan played the gong during the meditation.

TO END: Inhale, hold the breath for 45 seconds, and exhale. Repeat this sequence two more times, each time holding the breath as long as is comfortable.

COMMENTS

We are adjusting the two areas that we call the temples. These areas are more important that we know. In the ancient wisdom, they are known as the main centers of each zone of interconnection and intercommunication.

Connecting the Third & Fifth Chakras

1. Sit in Easy Pose. Bring the hands palm down in front of you parallel to the ground. Move the hands up and down alternately as if you are bouncing a ball. Feel the magnetic relationship to the ball of energy in the palms. Eyes are closed. **1 1/2 minutes**.

2. Keep moving the hands and begin breathing through the mouth as you create a sound like a baboon: Baboon Breath. Eyes are closed. Go inside and make your own rhythm and your own pattern. **5 minutes**.

Get this monkey out of your mind and system. Don't be shy. This will stimulate the parathyroid and you will burn up your sick dreams and your memories. By playing that ball, you will be able to control the psycho-magnetic energy.

3. Continue bouncing the hands with Baboon Breath as you bring your hands into Buddhi Mudra: Mercury (pinkie) finger touches the thumb, and the other three fingers are straight. Eyes remain closed. **2 minutes**.

4. Make the hands into a fist, with thumbs inside touching the Mercury Mound. Bring the arms out to the sides, straight from the shoulders with the fists facing up. Vigorously move the fists toward the front of the shoulders, contracting the bicep. As the fist comes toward the shoulder, resist so that you don't actually touch the shoulder. Continue a loud Baboon Breath. **2 1/2 minutes**.

You are stimulating the heart meridian inside the elbow.

5. Inhale deep and bring the hands to the Heart Center, right hand over left. Press hard, both hands flat. Breathe long and deep as you continue pressing hard. After **1 minute** begin to sing along with *Adi Shakti* by Nirinjan Kaur. After **1 minute** more begin singing from the navel. Move the navel as you sing. Combine the Third Chakra and the Fifth Chakra. **11 minutes**.

TO END: Inhale deeply. Hold 20 seconds and circulate the breath. Let it oxygenate the blood. Exhale. Inhale and repeat. Inhale, hold for **15 seconds** as you press the rib cage. Exhale and relax.

BREAK: Encourage students to walk around.

Continued on the next page.

Connecting the Third & Fifth Chakras

6. Interlock the fingers above the head. Thumbs can be interlocked or tips touching. Make your own halo. Close the eyes. Pump the navel firmly with the simple rhythm of the mantra. Concentrate on the navel. Music: *Pavan Pavan* by Guru Shabd Singh. **7 minutes.** Keeping the mudra steady, begin singing loudly with the mantra. Move the navel firmly and sing with the tip of the tongue. **7 minutes.**

TO END: Inhale deeply, lock the fingers tightly and pull the arms away from each other. Hold the breath 20 seconds. Exhale. Repeat 3 more times, holding for 15 seconds each time.

We are going to change the serum of the spine many, many times, to reenergize our gray matter. . . when you are tense, you are uptight, you are not happy, your life is miserable, unfulfilled, "I am not enough, this is not enough . . ." Do you understand how much you hurt yourself by saying "I am not enough?" Let us test it out.

7. Stretch the arms straight out in front of you at shoulder height. Right hand is resting on top of the left hand, palms up, tips of fingers crossed and thumbs stretched away from the fingers. Don't let the hands move. Eyes are open and looking straight ahead; don't blink; fix your eyes on a single point.
Music: *Bountiful, Blissful, Beautiful* by Nirinjan Kaur. Sing along with the mantra for **7 minutes.** Close eyes and keep singing for 1 minute.

TO END: Inhale deeply. Hold 20 seconds. Exhale. Inhale, hold 15 seconds and release the breath powerfully. Inhale and hold 20 seconds and release the breath powerfully. Relax. **11 minutes.**

8. Shake the entire body. This is self acupuncture. Any part you shake will regroup itself in energy, cells will rebuild, health will return and energy will go where there are blocks. **1 minute.**

COMMENTS
After this kriya, drink as much water as you can. Normally with this course we require 50 to 80 ounces of water from this minute onward. And the fact is, if you drink the amount of water we require, you will get up at night about four times to go to the bathroom. And that's what is needed. The system has to be force-flushed.

Meditation for the Fifth Chakra

MUDRA: Sit in Easy Pose with a straight spine. The arms are straight and the hands are in Gyan Mudra (thumbs and first fingertips touching.) The wrists are resting on the knees, palms up.

EYES: Focus at the tip of the nose.

BANDH: Apply Jalandhar Bandh (Neck Lock), pulling the chin in and back. This should pressurize the back of the neck below the skull. Yogi Bhajan says that if applied correctly, you will feel this in the deltoid muscles.

MANTRA: Chant the following mantra with the root of the tongue:

Hamee Ham Brahm Ham
We are we, we are God

TIME: **22 minutes**.

COMMENTS

Do it 11 minutes daily for 18 months and your face will not age. It will give endurance, intuition and reverse disease.

Jalandhar Bandh: In Kundalini Yoga practice, especially while practicing meditations, Neck Lock is generally utilized. In this meditation, it is particuarly vital. For optimum benefit, lift the chest and sternum upward, while gently stretching the back of the chin toward the back of the neck. Head stays level. If applied correctly, you will feel this in the deltoid muscles, though the muscles of the neck and throat remain loose. The idea is to open the channels of the neck and head to the flow of energy.

Meditation for Intuitive Speaking & Applied Consciousness

Sit in Easy Pose.

MUDRA: Place your fingertips on the heart center with the finger nails touching. All four fingers touch the heart center gently. The thumbs extend upward. The fingers curve naturally into the Heart Center.

EYES: The eyes are focused at the tip of the nose.

MANTRA: Chant the mantra *Har* at the pace of one per second along with the *Tantric Har* recording. The Navel Point pumps automatically with this sound.
  a) Chant out loud for **3 minutes**.
  b) Then whisper with it for **4 minutes**.
  c) Then do it silently. Pump the navel and feel the sound at the heart center for **6 minutes**.
  d) Then extend the arms up with fingers spread wide and chant to distribute the energy for **90 seconds**.

TO END:
Inhale very deeply, make fists of your hands and press them on the chest hard. Exhale.
Inhale deeply again, press the fists on the Navel Point. Hold as long as you can. Exhale.
Inhale and make the fists next to the shoulders. Hold. Consolidate yourself and then relax.

COMMENTS

If you just listen to the sound and feel yourself say it, you will enter a meditative twilight zone. Go past that by feeling the sound in the fingertips and then the entire rib cage and then the entire body. Hear the subtle energy of the sound. There are six creative sounds that create our world: *Har Haray Haree Wha-Hay Guru*. Listen to the sound of *Har* as a creative, qualified word expressed by your being and the Being of All.

Meditation for Word Power

Sit in Easy Pose with erect spine.

MUDRA: Have hands in Gyan Mudra over knees or relaxed in the lap, the right hand resting in left with both palms up.

MANTRA: There is no mantra for this meditation although you may want to play the *Tantric Har* recording for rhythmic support.

EYES: Not specified.

BREATH: Inhale deeply, exhale and hold the breath out as long as comfortable. Then inhale deeply and immediately exhale again. Continue this breath pattern for 11 minutes as you do the following: As you hold the breath out, regularly pulse the Navel Point and the tip of the tongue together. Pull in the Navel Point and lift the tongue to strike the top of the mouth at the same time. The tongue must snap up as the navel snaps inward. It is a small precise movement. The mouth may be closed or relaxed and slightly open. You can silently imagine the *Har* sounds.

Meditation for the Secret Door of the Six Sounds

PART ONE

Sit straight in Easy Pose facing a partner. Interlock hands tightly with your partner's, pressing the fingers on the backs of the hands of your partner. Elbows are relaxed down.

EYES: Look straight into the partner's eyes, penetrate them and then close the eyes before starting.

MANTRA: Call in a monotone from the navel, in a firm rhythm:

Har Haray Haree

and partner answers:

Whaa-hay Guroo

TIME: Continue for **11 minutes**.

PART TWO

Hold the position and continue chanting in a whisper in call and answer style for **11 minutes**.

PART THREE

Hold the position and do Long Deep Breathing, filling yourself with air up from the Navel Point. Exercise self-control. Continue for **11 minutes**.

PART FOUR

Hold the position and do a heavy Breath of Fire. Try your best. Put in all your effort at the Navel Point. Continue for **90 seconds**.

TO END: Inhale deeply, hold and pull against each other's hands. Pull and stop yourself from being pulled! Exhale. Repeat 2 more times. Relax.

PART FIVE

Dance with the *"Bolay So Nihal"* recording for **3 to 11 minutes**.

Meditation to Listen with Simultaneous Recall

Sit in Easy Pose.

MUDRA: With the elbows bent down by the sides, raise the hands so they are at the side of and in front of each shoulder, palms facing forward. Make fists of the hands, thumbs on top of the fingers, and extend the index (Jupiter) and middle (Saturn) fingers up in a "V" or "peace sign."

EYES: Focus at the tip of the nose.

BREATH: Make your breathing very slow and complete.

MANTRA: Play a recording of the mantra for the final 11 minutes of the meditation. Meditate in silence; do not chant.

> ### *Wha-hay Guroo, Wha-hay Guroo,*
> ### *Wha-hay Guroo, Wha-hay Jeeo*

Listen to the sounds of the mantra. Stay alert and aware. The moment you start to meditate, your mind will start talking to you. Try to hear what your mind says to you. You will want to hear everything else, the whole world, but today you must hear your own mind. Stay with it. Each thought that passes now is from your subconscious. Listen to it. Perceive and understand it.

TIME: **31 minutes**. (Meditate silently for 20 minutes. For the last 11 minutes, play the music very softly.)

TO END: In the final minute, continue to meditate but flex and circle the spine with tension, and stretch the spine.

COMMENTS

If you do not have the capacity to hear yourself, you cannot hear others. When you cannot listen to another person or situation, there'll be no mutual understanding, and that's why life goes in error.

Solving Communication Problems

Sit in Easy Pose with the spine straight.

MUDRA: Touch the thumb and Mercury (pinkie) finger of one hand to the thumb and Mercury finger of the other hand. Bend the Sun (ring) fingers in toward the palms, but do not let them touch the palms. Leave the Jupiter (index) and Saturn (middle) fingers pointing straight up, but not touching.

MUSIC: Meditatively listen to *Beloved God*, the first song on Singh Kaur's *Peace Lagoon* recording.

TIME: Start with **11 minutes** and work up to **31 minutes**.

COMMENTS

This meditation activates the Mercury power of communication.

Meditation for Positive Communication

Sit in Easy Pose with an erect spine.

MUDRA: Raise both hands 9-12 inches in front of the chest so the arms are shoulder height, and the hands angle down from throat level toward the heart level. Both palms face the body, with the back of the right palm in the palm of the left hand. Fingers are straight and together. Fold the left thumb over the right palm, and fold the right thumb over the left thumb. The hands will have the fingers crossed and angled downwards. Once you create the mudra, stretch the shoulders forward comfortably.

EYES: Eyes are closed.

BREATH: Take a deep inhale and chant the mantra five times on a breath as you exhale. This takes 10-12 seconds. Then immediately inhale deeply through the nose.

MANTRA: In a smooth monotone chant:

Haree Haree Haree Haree Haree Haree Har

TIME: Continue up to **11 minutes** with the group.
On your own you can increase the time, with practice, up to **31 minutes**.

COMMENTS
Listen to your words as you speak them. Feel the sounds flow over the tongue and the tip of the tongue. Be fully present to each sound, and create a focused projection with your mind.

CHAPTER SIX

CONNECT TO
THE INFINITE

SERVING THE INFINITE

Identify With Your Own Infinity

"When I call on my Infinity, I can come through anything."
–Yogi Bhajan

Most of us want to feel connected to something beyond ourselves. For some it's community; for others it's a longing for the Beloved; still for others it's an unquenchable thirst to be one with the One, with God. Yet for many, that connection is tenuous at best. Kundalini Yoga offers each of us an opportunity to experience that connection again—through the breath and through mantra—we're led to the gates of Infinity and we're asked to knock. If we summon the courage, then we're met with the Infinity within and blessed to be healed by the experience of our own vastness. The God within and the God without merge into a single breath; this is grace. This is *Ek Ong Kaar Sat Gurprasad.*

"States of change, altered consciousness, are the primary requirement of all living beings. Each minute, each pattern, becomes the last measurement through which we can see change. We change because change is the law of life, which is vibratory self-existence. Each prana comes, rotates our body, gives us an experience, we see, we hear, we feel through these senses, and then it goes out again, taking the image of our state of consciousness at that moment. This cycle goes in and out all the time: this is the law of cosmic consciousness.

If you ever want to change your consciousness, you have to have an image, something to relate to. If you relate to Infinity, you can go unto Infinity. If you relate to the finite, then you go up to the finite; this is for you to decide. Nobody is going to decide this for you. It is wrong to decide another's consciousness. But if you have a longing to belong then the belonging will long to belong to you—that's a law. If you have a longing to belong then the belonging shall long to belong to you."[1]

As we enter the Aquarian Age, the sense of separation will only increase. People will experience a longing that they won't know how to fulfill. Remind them to connect to their inner Self, their higher Truth, their own Infinity. There are so many ways to remember and there are so many names to call upon. Call on the one that speaks to your own Infinity. Chant the Kundalini Bhakti Mantra and feel the delight of the *Ma,* the creative force of the universe vibrating through every cell of your being. Dance the dance of the breath. Breathe the breath that will carry your identity into the cosmos so that it can return to you changed; and you, in turn, can breathe yourself in, changed, again.

With each breath we are renewed in the identity of Infinity. God and me, me and God, are One. With these words we align our little self to our higher Self and come to understand that we are part of something greater and that something greater dwells within us, too. We are not separate. The duality we experience is an illusion. Everything is God and everything is Good. As we connect, we increase our vitality to face life with strength, courage and *cherdi kala*—ever-rising spirit. We attach our identity to our own Infinity and we are transformed. In each moment, with each breath, we allow the Infinite to dwell here, within us, as a human, simply being.

1 © The Teachings of Yogi Bhajan, April 26, 1973

Subagh Kriya

This is a 5-part Kriya. Give each of the five parts equal time. 3 minutes each, 5 minutes each, or 11 minutes each.

1. Sit in Easy Pose with a straight spine. Allow your upper arms to be relaxed, with the elbows bent and the palms in front of the chest. Strike the outer sides of the hands together, forcefully hitting the area from the base of the Mercury (pinkie finger) to the base of the palm. This area is called the Moon area. Next, turn the palms to face down and strike the sides of the Jupiter (index) fingers together. Alternately strike the Moon area and the Jupiter area as you chant **Har** with the tip of your tongue, pulling the navel with each **Har**. Your eyes are focused at the tip of the nose. This meditation was taught to the rhythm of *Tantric Har* by Simran Kaur.

I'm going to give you a very handy tool, one that you can use anywhere, and you'll become rich. To become rich and prosperous, with wealth and values, is to have the strength to come through. It means that transmissions from your brain and the power of your intuition can immediately tell you what to do.

2. Stretch the arms out to the sides and up at a 60-degree angle. Spread the fingers wide, making them stiff. The palms face forward. Cross the arms in front of your face. Alternate the position of the arms as they cross: first the left arm crosses in front of the right and then the right arm crosses in front of the left. Continue crossing the arms, keeping the elbows straight and the fingers open and stiff. This movement is also done to the rhythm of *Tantric Har* by Simran Kaur, but this time you do not chant.

Subagh Kriya

3. Keep the arms out and up at 60 degrees as in the previous exercise. Make a fist around your thumb, squeezing your thumb tightly. Move your arms in small backward circles as you continue squeezing your thumb. Your arms are stretched and the elbows stay straight. Chant the mantra *God* powerfully form your navel. One backward circle of the arms equals one repetition of *God*. The speed and rhythm of the chanting is the same as in the previous exercises. Move powerfully so that your entire spine shakes, you may even be lifted slightly up off the ground by the movement.

4. Bend the arms so that the elbows point to the sides. The forearms are parallel to the floor and the palms face the body around the level of the diaphragm. The hands move alternately up and down between the heart and navel. The right hand moves up a few inches as the left hand moves down. The left hand moves up as the right hand moves down. As the hands move, chant *Har Haray Haree, Wha-hay Guroo* in a deep monotone with one repetition of the mantra approximately every 4 seconds. Chant from your navel.

TIME: If you are practicing the exercises for **11 minutes** each, then you will chant the mantra out loud for **6 minutes**, whisper it strongly for **3 minutes** and then whistle it for **2 minutes**.

If you are practicing the exercises for **3 minutes** each, then you will chant the mantra out loud for **1 minute**, whisper it strongly for **1 minute**, and then whistle it for **1 minute**.

If you are practicing the exercises for **5 minutes** each, then you will chant the mantra out loud for **3 minutes**, whisper it strongly for **1 minute**, and then whistle it for **1 minute**.

5. One Minute Breath. Bend the elbows and rest the right forearm on the left forearm, with the palms down. The arms are held in front of the body at shoulder height. Close the eyes, keep your arms steady. Keep the spine straight and your arms parallel to the floor. Breathe slowly and deeply so that one breath takes a full minute. Inhale for **20 seconds**, hold for **20 seconds**, and exhale for **20 seconds**.

Linking with the Infinite

Sit is Easy Pose with your spine straight, chin in and chest out.

MUDRA & BREATH: Block the right nostril with the right index finger. inhale through the left nostril. Chant **Ong** in the long form, in such a way that the sound comes out of the left nostril. The entire exhalation is one recitation of **Ong** (15-20 seconds). The mouth is open but the sound does not come out of the mouth. (Do not suppress a sneeze.)

Switch sides. Close off the left nostril with the left index finger. Inhale through the right nostril. Chant **Ong** in such a way that the sound comes out of the right nostril. The mouth is open but the sound does not come out of the mouth.

TIME: **3-11 minutes** on each side.

Observe the following rules in practicing this meditation:
• Rest afterwards. Do not immediately resume normal activity.
• The breath should not come out of the mouth.
• The breath vibrates under the back of the upper palate.
• Make sure that if you need to blow your nose, take the time to do it even during chanting. Be sensible and do not do this meditation with clogged sinuses.

COMMENTS

This meditation powerfully activates both sides of the brain. It opens up the mind and is most powerful depending on which nostril is currently active.

The sages for ages who developed Kundalini Yoga sat and worked it out, from one person to the other. When they were certain that they had mastered the technique (what it is, how it is to be done, and what are the results), they had the instructions carved onto bamboo sheets. It took years and years to perfect the teaching of this technique.

Develop this meditation slowly, gently, and with sophistication. It is not an ego trip. Begin with 3 minutes on each side and, with practice, work up to the full time of 11 minutes on each side.

Without breath, the body has no value. Breath is the principle of life. Between God and you, it is the link. Meditation on breath is the highest meditation. God is known as *Praanpathi*, the Master of breath, and a person is known as *praanee*, one who lives on the breath. So your relationship is between the *Praanpathi* and the *praanee*. You can color it: Christian breath, Jewish breath, Hindu breath, Sikh breath, Muslim breath, but that doesn't make any sense. Breath is breath. Between the *Praanpathi*, the holder of the breath, and the breathing self, that is *praanee*, there is a direct relationship and we can experience that though this kriya.

Meditation to Teach You How to Pray

MUDRA: Interlace the fingers so the left Mercury (pinkie) finger is on the outside. Extend the Jupiter (index) fingers up straight. Cross the thumbs, so right is over left. Place this mudra in front of the Heart Center so the thumbs are very close to the chest, and the Jupiter fingers are pointing straight up toward the ceiling. The elbows will be bent.

EYES: Closed or 1/10th open.

MEDITATIVE FOCUS: Build an image of yourself. You are still and radiant. Your breath is slow, deep and meditative. Imagine you are sitting on the top of Mount Everest, so all the world is around you. Consider your spine is like a tube of light. There is light between the base of your neck and the base where you are sitting. Now it is sending out light rays. You can send waves to the entire globe with each thought. Your prayer is like a stone, which is dropped in the middle of some water. It creates waves and ripples. Feel yourself as the waves and ripples go on and on unto Infinity. The power of your soul is the pure power. Let the power of your soul vibrate out. It has no limit or boundary. With each breath and with the ripples of your heartbeat, project, bless, and be blessed. Merge in Infinity and let Infinity find you too.

TIME: Do it for **11 minutes** to a maximum **31 minutes**. Done for 15 minute in class.

TO END: Do heavy Breath of Fire, holding the position, to awaken yourself out of the meditation. Continue for 1 minute.

Then stretch the arms out to the sides, forearms bent up at about a 45-degree angle, palms down. Begin circling just the hands, right hand counterclockwise and left hand clockwise, in 6-inch circles. Don't just circle them. Stop every so often as the hands are up and out to the sides, and flutter your fingers a little, as if you are sending off energy to the environment and space around you.

Kundalini Bhakti Mantra
Adi Shakti Namo Namo

This devotional mantra (a Bhakti mantra), invokes the primary Creative Power which is manifest as the feminine. It calls upon the Mother Power. It will help you to be free of the insecurities which block freedom of action. By meditating on it one can obtain a deeper understanding of the constant interplay between the manifest and the unmanifest qualities of the cosmos and consciousness.

Adi	Shakti	Adi	Shakti	Adi	Shakti	Na - mo	Na - mo
Sarab	Shakti	Sarab	Shakti	Sarab	Shakti	Na - mo	Na - mo
Pritham Bhagvati		Pritham Bhagvati		Pritham Bhagvati		Na - mo	Na - mo
Kunda- lini		Mata	Shakti	Mata	Shakti	Na - mo	Na- mo

I bow to the Primal Power.
I bow to the all Encompassing Power and Energy.
I bow to that through which God creates.
I bow to the creative power of the kundalini, the Divine Mother Power.

A WOMAN'S PERSONAL MANTRA AS AN ESSENTIAL DAILY PRACTICE
This powerful mantra belongs to all women to call upon any time. She can chant it freely and powerfully at will, any time.

WITH CELESTIAL COMMUNICATION
This mantra can be experienced powerfully by adding Celestial Communication. Celestial Communication is mudra in motion. A tool for mental relaxation, it is meditation with mantra and movement of the arms and upper body. The meaning of the mantra is expressed through movement. The mantra will move the spirit, and at the same time, the head and feelings will be heard. Yogi Bhajan describes its impact:

"Everything comes from stress. If you want to get rid of this inner-grown stress, here is one solution. There's no power more than the power of the word, and when the word is formed through the body, the entire being is purified, relaxed..."

You can create your own Celestial Communiction movements, or learn already developed sequences.

WITH SPECIFIC MEDITATIONS
Yogi Bhajan taught this mantra with several meditations, such as in Adi Shakti Meditation for Vitality and Meditation to Call on the Divine Mother which are in the *I Am a Woman* Yoga Manual.

Isht Sodhana Mantra Kriya
Evening Meditation for Effective Prayer

Sit in Easy Pose with a straight spine, and feel that you are sitting on the earth, and your head is in the ethers.

MUDRA: The hands are in Gyan Mudra relaxed over the knees.

EYES: Closed and rolled upward. Mentally focus through the Brow Point.

BREATH: Chant the entire mantra on one deep breath. Inhale and continue.

MEDITATIVE FOCUS: Imagine your head is in the sky and the Heavens—the Ether—where the color is blue, and you are sitting on the Earth where the color is gray. Allow these colors to cover your body. Between your eyebrows and the top of your head is blue ether, from your waistline down it is a pure gray, and from the Heart Center radiates a brilliant whiteness.

MANTRA: Chant the mantra in one breath:

Dhartee hai akaash hai, guroo raam daas hai
The Earth realm is. The etheric realm is. Guru Ram Das is.

As you chant *dhartee hai* imagine the gray color. As you chant *akaash hai* imagine a beautiful deep dark royal blue color. As you chant *guroo raam daas hai* bring the meditation to your Heart Center and imagine a brilliant whiteness. A whiteness as bright as a sun, but white-white, not a golden sun-white.

TIME: Continue for **11 minutes**. You can increase it to **31 minutes**.

TO END: Inhale deeply and radiate pure white, as if you have dissolved yourself into Infinity, and Infinity has merged into you.

COMMENTS

This meditation gives a person the power to penetrate through the entire cosmos. It uses the impact of the word and a potent visualization for the elements. Every prayer becomes effective with this steady practice. It is called *Isht Sodhana Mantra Kriya*. *Isht* means the defined, experienced God; sodhana means to purify; straighten out. One is isht sodhana who purifies the God in experience. The underworld, the world and the world of God shall serve that individual who can perfect this Isht Sodhana Mantra.

This meditation should be practiced in the evening. The best time is at sunset. It is all right to chant it in the morning, but when you do it as a personal practice to get the essence of it, you have to do it in the evening.

It is a perfect mantra. It is *ashtang*, an eight-beat mantra. It has eight vibratory imprints and effects. In *Naad*, its subtle sound, is perfect. This will give you the power to know your past, present and future—and whatever a person anywhere has to think, say or do. You will know it, before they do. That is the stillness, effectiveness and sensitivity it can give you.

Me & God Are One

Sit in an easy cross-legged position, or sit in a chair with a straight spine and both feet flat on the floor.

MUDRA: Place your hands in Gyan Mudra, thumb and index finger touching each other with the other fingers straight. With the hands in this position, cross the right hand over the left at the heart center, but not touching the chest. The right palm is against the back of the left hand.

EYES: Eyes are closed.

MANTRA: Repeat the affirmation with Yogi Bhajan using the *Destiny* CD from Kundalini Research Institute.

God and Me, Me and God, Are One

TIME: **11-31 minutes**.

TO END: Inhale, suspend the breath. Exhale, release the mudra. Relax.

Meditation on the Different Names of God

Sit in a meditative posture.

EYES: Close the eyes.

MUSIC: Meditate on the various Names of God on Matamandir Singh's recording.

TIME: **5 minutes**.

TO END: Inhale and relax.

COMMENTS: Every religion has one word:

Jaa-ho-vaah — Yaah

Haa-le-lu-ja — Haa

Laa-ay-laa — Laa

Raa-maa — Raa

Saa-taa Naa-maa — Saa

COMMENTS

They don't have more than one sound, yet still man fights with each other. Man and his world, and his kingdom, and man dividing each other, "I am black, I am yellow, I am pink, I am gold, I am white, I am this." The fighting has never stopped. Neither religion has stopped it, nor geography has stopped it, nothing, because basically there is a greed. The idea is, "God is impotent, He will do nothing, I have to do everything." The fight is between "I" and "Thou." But the Teacher belongs to "Thou," not "I."

We have practiced religion for thousands of years, we have never practiced reality. Reality is: We are spirit. We are always spirit. When we are not spirit, we are called "Dead." And when we are alive and we do not recognize spirit, we are "Super Dead." The one whose Third Eye opens is that one whose "I" belongs to "Thou."

Listening to Angelic Whispers

Sit down very calmly and quietly, with a straight spine.

MUDRA: Put your hands on opposite shoulders. Your arms must cross. Hold your shoulders well, the arms relaxed on the chest.

EYES: Close your eyes.

MANTRA: Listen to the recording of the mantra:

> **Ardaas bhayee, amar daas guroo,**
> **Amar daas guroo, ardaas bhayee,**
> **Raam daas guroo, raam daas guroo,**
> **Raam daas guroo, sachee sahee.**

The Grace of Guru Amar Das (who is the Hope of the hopeless) and Guru Ram Das (who is the King of the yogis and Bestower of blessings— past, present, and future) guarantee the prayer will be answered and all one's needs provided for.

As you listen to the instruments play this tune, whistle with it. Hear the sound of the whistle at the Brow Point. Keep the eyes closed. Inside of your self, be very calm, quiet. This is a posture of peace. Continue 15-31 minutes. Then begin long, slow, deep breathing. Mentally listen to the echo of your whistling. Hear the sound you created before. Bring your unison power of the mind, the subtle *sattvic guna* of the mind, to listen. Once you learn to listen this way, you can listen in exactly the same way to what God's Will is. When you can still the mind, refine it, command its guna, then you can listen to God's Will, discern what it is, then act. Life will be very easy, content, and fulfilled. In the Bible you are told the same thing. There is a word called "Behold." Behold yourself. Be within yourself and listen.

TIME: Continue for **3 to 11 minutes.**

TO END: End with three powerful breaths: inhale deep through the nose, hold for 5-10 seconds. Exhale powerfully through the mouth. As you hold the breath in, put all the pressure downward on your shoulders with your hands. Press them down, and keep the spine steady and straight. Repeat the breath three times. Relax.

COMMENTS

This meditation will refine the *sattvic guna* of your mind.

Kundalini Laya Yoga Shakti Meditation

Sit in Easy Pose with the spine straight.

MUDRA: Put the palms together in Prayer Pose at the center of the chest.

MANTRA & MEDITATIVE FOCUS: Focus through the Brow Point. Chant:

Ek ong kaar (uh)

Saa taa naa maa (uh)

Siree whaa (uh)

Hay gu-roo

One Creator Creation
True Identity
Great Indescribable Wisdom

The chant is very precise. On **Ek** pull in the navel. On each "uh" lift the diaphragm up firmly. (The sound "uh" is not part of the mantra; rather the sound made by the force of the lifting of the diaphragm.) Relax the navel and abdomen on **Hay guroo**. The sound has a spin to it. It is a 3 -1/2 cycle rhythm. As you chant, imagine energy and sound spiraling up and around the spinal cord in a right-handed helix. Start at the base of the spine as you initiate the energy from the navel. End with focus over the head to the Cosmos on **Hay guroo**.

TIME: Continue for **31 minutes**.

COMMENTS

This extraordinary Laya Yoga Chant will bring your soul and destiny present. It will suspend you above conflicts attracted by success and the activity of the Positive Mind. It will let your activity serve your purpose. It will make you creative and focused on your real priorities, and help you sacrifice what is needed to accomplish them.

CHAPTER SEVEN

PROJECT
YOUR DESTINY

SERVING THE INFINITE

Vibrate Your Highest Consciousness

"As a Teacher you have to shape your own destiny and experience it before you shape somebody else's destiny. It's your responsibility."[1]
–Yogi Bhajan

There are many ways to interpret one's destiny. Our natal astrology chart gives us some clues to the obstacles and opportunities in our path; our numerology gives us a glimpse of our latent potential; our spiritual name gives us something to strive for as we grow toward spiritual maturity; and our family background gives us our foundation. But these are all based in time and space—and they are only part of the picture. We have the opportunity to live beyond time and space, beyond our karma, and dwell in dharma. We have the opportunity to define our own destinies in consciousness through applied intelligence, meditation and reflection, and the grist that is a sadh sangat.

As teachers and yogis, our destiny is defined by our projection. On any given day, we may not feel like a teacher. We may not be in the mood to uplift someone else, or lend a helping hand. We may be fatigued, or road weary, or agitated. But we show up. We dress the part. We expand our Pranic and Radiant Bodies and we serve. We live our destiny every time we show up to teach. On any given day we may not feel like a yogi. We may be sore, or tired, or stiff; but we take that first conscious breath and we do our practice: ishnaan, pranayam, asana, chanting and prayer. We live our destiny each time we deliver ourselves to our sadhana.

To project our own destiny doesn't mean we get to decide our futures or even our fate. The Unseen Hand is still at work; but it does mean that we have an opportunity to align our will to God's Will; our purpose to the Guru's purposes; to get in line with what is and vibrate our highest consciousness. We have the opportunity to live a life of intention and receive the fruits of that intention— not grasp for them. The moment we reach out to take something we believe we deserve, we've already lost the game. Living one's destiny is a balancing act between making right effort and receiving the gifts of grace. It is the balancing act of Shakti and Bhakti—personal power and humility in devotion.

Projecting our destiny is simply a commitment—to our highest identity, in every moment, and with every breath. When are you not a teacher? When are you not a yogi? When are you not a spiritual being? Projection is simply a recognition of the reality of our identity and a commitment to serve that identity in consciousness. The kriyas and meditations in this chapter facilitate that recognition and alignment with our highest truth.

"The elementary self of God is '*Sat Satya Satiaam.*' '*Sat*'—my true essence is *Sat*. '*Satya*'—the power of my true essence. "*Satiaam*"—in true essence, I am. "*Sat Naam*"—*Naam* means a noun. Noun is the name of a person, place, or thing. So, *Sat Naam* means "Truth is my identity."

"That's my *Naam*, that's my name. When I ask for a spiritual name, that name describes my distance, my destiny, and my guiding word. 'In the Beginning was the Word, the Word was with God, and the Word was God.'[2] It has to be calculated. I don't know what's so difficult. The purpose of life is to cover a distance. If it doesn't cover the distance, you'll keep on going through the cycle of birth and death."[3]

1 Master's Touch, page 147
2 John 1:1
3 Master's Touch p. 136

Pran Bandha Mantra Meditation
to Rewrite the Destiny in Your Hands

Sit in Easy Pose.

MUDRA: Palms are flat and facing the body slightly higher than the Heart Center, and about 12 inches away from the body. Cross the hands at the wrists with the left palm closest to the body. The fingers of the right hand will be slanted toward the left, and the fingers of the left hand will be slanted toward the right. The thumbs of both hands will meet in the center, directly in line with each other, one on top of the other.

EYES: Stare at the tip of the nose, but then look down past the nose into the palms.

BREATH & MEDITATIVE VISUALIZATION:
Look down into the palms and read the lines of the hand with a long slow breath for **11 minutes**.
Continue to meditate. Begin chanting with the recording *Pavan Pavan* by Guru Shabd Singh. Consciously rewrite the lines of your hands as you listen to what you say, process the *Naad*, the current of subtle sounds. Continue for another **20 minutes**.

MANTRA:
Pavan pavan pavan pavan
Par paraa pavan guroo
Pavan guroo whaa-hay guroo
Whaa-hay guroo pavan guroo

TIME: Total of **31 minutes**.

TO END: Inhale deeply and stiffen the spine tightly. Hold for 20 seconds. Exhale. Inhale, make every muscle from head to tailbone like steel. Hold 20-25 seconds. Exhale. Inhale, and hold a final time. Make your spine like a steel rod, going vertebrae by vertebrae. Hold up to 30 seconds according to your capacity. Exhale and relax.

Hast Kriya: Earth to Heaven

Sit in Easy Pose.

MUDRA: Extend the Jupiter (index) finger on both hands. Lock the other fingers down with the thumbs.

MUSIC & MOVEMENT: Coordinate your movement with the recording *Sat Nam Wahe Guru #2* by Jagjit Singh.

Touch the Jupiter fingers to the floor on either side of you when the ragi chants *Sat*.
Touch the Jupiter fingers together over the top of your head when the ragi chants *Naam*.
Touch the Jupiter fingers to the floor on either side of you when the ragi chants *Sat*.
Touch the Jupiter fingers together over the top of your head when the ragi chants *Naam*.
Touch your Jupiter fingers to the floor on either side of you when the ragi chants *Whaa-hay*.
Touch your Jupiter fingers together over the top of your head when the ragi chants *Guroo*.
Touch your Jupiter fingers to the floor on either side of you when the ragi chants *Whaa-hay*.
Touch your Jupiter fingers together over the top of your head when the ragi chants *Guroo*.

TIME: **22 minutes**.

COMMENTS

This kriya renews the nervous system and can help nerve pain and sciatica. If you do this Kriya for 22 minutes a day, you can totally change your personality. Power will descend from above and clean you out. Anger and obnoxiousness will disappear from your personality.

This kriya is so powerful it can hold the Hand of God; so powerful it can hold the hand of death. *Sat Naam Whaa-hay Guroo* is a Jupiter mantra. The most graceful power and knowledge comes from Jupiter. Jupiter controls the medulla oblongata, the neurological center of the brain, and the three rings of the brain stem.

Meditation For Awareness & to Become Strategic

Sit straight in Easy Pose.

MUDRA: Interlace the fingers, one hand into the other. Extend the Mercury (pinkie) fingers, Sun (ring) fingers, and Saturn (middle) fingers so they touch the same fingers of the opposite hand, and so all point straight up. Separate the base of the palms about 4 inches so the three fingers form a teepee, and a round space opens between the two index fingers, on top, and the two thumbs, below. Raise this mudra up to your face and put your nose in the opening between index fingers and thumbs. The index fingers rest near the bridge of the nose. The thumbs cross just under the nose but do not block the nostrils. The other fingers point straight up. Elbows are relaxed.

MANTRA: Focus at the Brow Point and chant the following mantra.

Har har gobinday	*Sustains You*
Har har mukanday	*Liberates You*
Har har udaaray	*Elevates You*
Har har apaaray	*Delivers You Across*
Har har hareeang	*Destroys All*
Har har kareeang	*Creates All*
Har har nirnaamay	*Beyond Category & Name*
Har har akaamay	*Beyond Desire*

As you chant each beat of the mantra, press the tips of the three fingers in sequence. Begin with the middle fingertips pressing firmly on *Har*. Then the ring fingers on the next *Har*, and finally the little fingertips on *Gobinday*. Then press the little fingertips on *Har*, the ring finger on the second *Har* and the middle fingers on *Mukanday* and continue in this way through all 8 lines of the mantra, moving back and forth along the fingertips. As you chant these motions become smooth and automatic. Then your attention goes deep into the sound itself.

TIME: Continue for **11 to 31 minutes**.

TO END: Inhale deeply, hold, and focus at the Brow Point. Exhale powerfully through the mouth. Repeat this final breath sequence three times, and relax.

COMMENTS

This meditation develops your ability to increase your awareness of the meanings and consequences in events that others do not. Your agenda is impersonally personal. You become strategic, and don't mind losing a battle if you win the war. You can recognize and arrange resources masterfully. You may not manage them operationally, but you can recognize, attract, and gather them.

Develop Your Hidden Greatness

PART ONE

Sit straight. The left palm is facing down under the chin, with forearm parallel to the ground. The right hand comes to meet the middle finger of the left hand at the center of the palm, fingers pointing up to the sky. The hands are long and straight, fingers together. You are bifurcating the angles.

EYES: For all three parts of this kriya, eyes are focused at the tip of the nose.

BREATH: Breathe long and deep, from the lower area of the belly. Exhale slowly and completely through the O of the mouth. Yogiji demonstrates a very long inhalation, from the lower belly to the collar bones. You expand with the breath about an inch and a half. **20 minutes**.

This is a most sacred exercise in Kundalini Yoga and gives people the entire universe.

PART TWO

Switch hands. The right palm is facing down under the chin, with forearm parallel to the ground. The left hand comes to meet the middle finger of the right hand at the center of the palm, fingers pointing up. The hands are long and straight, fingers together.

MANTRA: Sing with *Har Singh Nar Singh* by Nirinjan Kaur.

5 minutes.

PART THREE

   a) Bring the thumbs just above the eyebrows at either side of the Third Eye Point. Press the thumbs into the brow and allow the hands to be in Prayer Pose.

MANTRA: Sing with *Ong Namo Guru Dev Namo* by Nirinjan Kaur. **1 1/2 minutes**.
   b) Whistle with the breath. **1 1/2 minutes**.
   c) Keeping the mudra, begin Long Deep Breathing and exhale through the rounded mouth, as in Part One. **3 minutes**.
   d) Arms at 60 degrees hands open and palms facing the sky. Begin Breath of Fire. Use the strength of the navel. **30 seconds**.
   e) Inhale deep and put both hands in the lap, right hand resting in the left. **2 minutes**.

Become thoughtless. "I forgive my thoughts; I forgive the universe; I forgive my friends." Forgiveness should override everything. Whatever is bothering you, whatever you hate, whatever you don't like, right now just feel an angel is before you and you are willing to go with him and merge in infinity. Are you afraid? Just drop the fear and proceed. All negativity, all negative thoughts must go thoughtless. "I am pure; I am divine; I am human: I am a creature of God. My faculties are divine."

TO END: Inhale deep. Squeeze. Exhale Cannon Breath. 3 times. Squeeze everything.

Kriya with Laya Yoga Kundalini Mantra

Sit in Easy Pose.

MUDRA: Hands in Venus Lock, arms parallel to the ground extended forward with the thumbs up and pulled back.

EYES: Eyes are open and fixed, looking through the V at the top of the thumbs. You should feel the pulse in your palms.

MANTRA: Chant aloud the 3 1/2 cycle Laya Yoga Kundalini Mantra:

Ek Ong Kaar (uh), Sa-ta Naam (uh),
Siree Whaa (uh), Hay Guroo

The "uh" represents pulling a powerful Diaphragm Lock; it is not part of the mantra.

TIME: Continue for at least **11 minutes**. 31 minutes is good. Maximum time is 2 hours 55 minutes 6 seconds.

TO END: Inhale, stretch the arms up high, as far as possible, hold, then exhale. Repeat 3 times.

COMMENTS:

This kriya is the most powerful in its effectiveness next to Sat Kriya. It merges the mind-body-soul into one vibrational effect. All glands and the rate of breath are affected. If done for the maximum time of 2 hours 55 minutes 6 seconds, one achieves a state of consciousness for perfect physical vibratory projection.

Gathering Energy for Creativity

Sit in a meditative pose with spine erect.

MUDRA: Arms by the sides with elbows bent to 90 degrees and palms facing each other at the level of the navel.

EYES: Eyes are 1/10th open or looking down the nose.

MANTRA: Chant the mantra:

Har har har har gobinday	*God God God God Sustainer*
Har har har har mukanday	*God God God God Liberator*
Har har har har udaaray	*God God God God Uplifter*
Har har har har apaaray	*God God God God Carrying Through*
Har har har har hareeang	*God God God God Destroyer of All*
Har har har har kareeang	*God God God God Creator of All*
Har har har har nirnaamay	*God God God God Beyond Category*
Har har har har akaamay	*God God God God Beyond Desire*

With each chant of the sound *Har* pulse the hands in toward each other then back out. The movement is about 6 inches. It is quick, forceful, and precise. Hold the hands still for the other sounds such as *Gobinday*.

TIME: Continue for **31 minutes**.

TO END: Inhale deeply, tighten the forearms, hands, and fingers. Focus at the Brow Point. Exhale powerfully through the mouth. Do this three times. Relax.

COMMENTS

This meditation gives the ability to enhance, extend, and utilize anything that enters your sense of domain. The joy of intelligent effective action is all around you. When balanced you put things into sequences that lead to desired consequences. You organize resources in your self and others to deliver a project, goal, and creation. You quickly discern what is your task and what is not.

Beaming & Creating the Future

Sit in Easy Pose. Stretch the spine up and become very still.

EYES: Eyes are closed.

MUDRA: Relax the hands in Gyan Mudra across the knees.

PART ONE

Drink the breath in a single, deep, long sip through a rounded mouth. Close the mouth and exhale through the nose, slowly and completely. **7-15 minutes**.

PART TWO

Inhale and hold the breath comfortably. As you suspend the breath in, meditate on zero. Think in this way:

> "All is zero; I am zero; each thought is zero; my pain is zero;
> that problem is zero; that illness is zero."

Meditate on all negative, emotional, mental and physical conditions and situations. As each thing crosses the mind, bring it to zero—a single point of light, a small, insignificant non-existence. Exhale and repeat. Breathe in a comfortable rhythm. **7-11 minutes**.

PART THREE

Think of the quality or condition you most desire for your complete happiness and growth. Summarize it in a single word like "Wealth," "Health," "Relationship," "Guidance," "Knowledge," "Luck." It has to be one word. Lock on that word and thought. Visualize facets of it. Inhale and suspend the breath as you beam the thought in a continuous stream. Lock onto it. Relax the breath as needed. **5-15 minutes**.

TO END: Inhale and move the shoulders, arms and spine. Then stretch the arms up, spread the fingers wide, and breathe deeply a few times.

COMMENTS

After clearing the mind of other distracting thoughts and attachments, it has tremendous capacity and creativity when focused and beaming. Use that beaming faculty. Become still and project the mind to create your future and your relationship to the world. The best way to practice this is on an empty stomach with only liquids taken during the day.

CHAPTER EIGHT

EXPERIENCING
GROUP CONSCIOUSNESS

SERVING THE INFINITE

"O beautiful unknown Creator of this consciousness.
O part of my existence, give us, as a whole, the power
to live another day in peace, tranquility, grace and beauty.
Take away from us the power of negativity,
the power of self-condemnation, the power of self-negation
and inspire us to be loving, living, and shining in the light of the truth.
Give us the strength to walk on the path of righteous,
in unity, merging the tranquility of consciousness among us all in peace,
and happiness and joy. Give us the strength to be united
so that we can save ourselves from the tyranny of the coming times.
Give us the strength to live for each other so that
we may all live with grace and dignity. In thy name,
and with gratitude for thy kindness, we offer this day to you.
Give us the power to be ready for the next day in peace.
Sat Nam." [1]

–Yogi Bhajan

The Elevation of Group Consciousness

Kundalini Yoga takes us from individual consciousness, to group consciousness, to universal consciousness. This is the essential journey toward spiritual maturity. Yogi Bhajan shepherded our awareness through each of the three levels of consciousness, which he viewed as three strands of a rope, inextricably intertwined. Many want to skip over group consciousness and revel in the One, the universal consciousness, or simply enjoy the bliss of their own meditation; but it doesn't work that way.

Universal consciousness without the demands and tests of individual commitment and obligation to the group often generate pretention and hubris. Individual consciousness alone can deliver powerful skills and even pleasure, but can also be accompanied by an untamed, short-sighted, self-centered ego.

Group consciousness is an essential skill for the Aquarian Age and one of the highest human capacities. Yogi Bhajan admired thinking as a group—group consciousness—each person merging their skills and ideas in an atmosphere of trust, sport, dialogue and solution-oriented action. It requires integrity, dignity and the capacity to qualify the self within the Self. Group consciousness is a discipline, which cultivates tolerance and serves individual consciousness in dropping its own agendas and allowing for a profound recognition of the universality of all human beings. Coming to see the God in all is a vital step along the path. If you can see the God in your enemy as well as your friend; if you can call brother the one who has harmed you as well as the one who has served you, then you have begun to understand tolerance and planted the seeds of Group Consciousness.

Group consciousness supports both individual and universal consciousness. The miracle of group consciousness manifests in myriad ways. Often the convictions of a single person can change the dynamic of an entire group. Just as often, the group can persuade the lone voice of protest to compromise. But the truest miracle is when all the voices come together to find a third option—one that would never have realized outside of the group. This is the elevated consciousness, which arises in the presence of trust and mutuality.

The kriyas in this chapter give us an opportunity to work together, with the sound current, to transcend our individual psyche and experience the group psyche as we elevate and uplift our consciousness to the universal consciousness which lives in the sound current. It is said that those who play together, stay together. So play with these kriyas and create the unity in each clap of the hand, each beat of the drum, each note of the song.

Balance the Mind in the Group Energy

1. Sit in Easy Pose. Sit very calm and quiet. Close the eyes. Bring the hands to the Brow Point in Prayer Pose with the thumbs locked. Begin moving in counter-clockwise circles from the pelvis all the way up the spine including the hands. Keep the hands above the eyebrows. Matamandir Singh's *Halleluiah* is played. Start singing with it after **12 minutes**. Inhale. Exhale and immediately move into the next exercise. Total: **20 minutes**.

You close your eyes and worship God. It is called Arta. It's actually a self-worship if you really want to understand. It is called Jan Puja—self-worship. Loosen your pelvic bone. Move your own universe. Get into a state of ecstasy.

2. Hold hands with one another and close your eyes. No hand should be single. Sit with chin in and chest out. Sit straight. Concentrate at the soft-spot at the crown of the head—the 10th gate. Breathe long and deep. Breathe consciously. Be steady. This meditation is done in silence. **15 minutes**. Inhale deep and release your hands. Exhale and immediately move into the next exercise.

If you can concentrate on this point at the time of death, the scripture says you go straight to God. This is the time to prove to yourself that you and God are One. You can free yourself of all diseases at this time.

3. Bring the forearm to 90 degrees so that the hands are above the shoulders with the fingers open. Begin making counter-clockwise circles with your arms and upper body. Sing along with Niranjan Kaur's *Every Heartbeat*. Move the energy in all parts of you. **5 minutes**. Inhale. Exhale and quickly move into the next exercise.

As you complete this exercise, look around and choose a partner as you get ready for the next exercise.

4. Stand up and dance with a partner. Punjabi Drum music is played.
    a. Look into the eyes of your partner. Move your hips. Move your arms. Hands stay above the head as you dance. **2 1/2 minutes**.
    b. Dance freely moving your waist; hands can move as you like. **4 1/2 minutes**.
    c. Begin to clap your hands. This removes arthritis. **30 seconds**.

Balance the Mind in the Group Energy

5. Sit in groups of four and play patty-cake.
   a) Clap your hands.
   b) Then turn and clap hands with your partner.
   c) Clap your hands then clap hands with the person sitting across from you
   d) Clap your hands then turn to the opposite side and clap hands with your other partner.
   2 minutes.

6. Still in your groups:
   a) Begin chanting *Har* with the tip of the tongue on every clap of the hands. **1 minute.**
   b) Begin chanting *'I God'* as you clap your hands and *'You God'* as you clap your partner's hands. **1 minute.**

7. Inhale deep and raise the hands up—as if you were surrendering. Concentrate at the 10th gate. **1 1/2 minutes**.

TO END: Inhale deep and hold tight; synchronize the body and spread the fingers. Cannon Breath exhale. Repeat twice more. Relax.

5a & 6a

5b & 6b

5c

7

5d

Truth & Oneness

PART ONE—AFFIRMATION FOR SELF-LOVE

Sit straight in a cross-legged position.

MUDRA & MOVEMENT:

Place your right hand on your heart and say, "*My heart, I love you.*"

Place your right hand on the eyes and say, "*My eyes, I love you.*"

Move to the top of your head and say, "*My head, I love you.*"

At the Navel Point say, "*I love you.*"

And placing your hands on both your knees say, "*I love you.*"

COMMENTS: Mankind is divided by religions, religions are divided by sects, sects are divided by cults, cults are divided by frictions. We still live in a cave called home, with the fire burning and the meat cooking. We do not live for each other. We live at each other or against each other. If you pay a little bit of attention to yourself and show love to yourself you will find yourself to be different. You have been taught to hate everything, and that what you do not hate will eat you up. This is your most stupid behavior.

PART TWO—AFFIRMATION FOR SELF-LOVE

Sit straight in a cross-legged position.

MUDRA: Raise the right hand by the shoulder, as if taking an oath, and say:

"*A teacher is not a preacher. A preacher is a preacher.*
A teacher is a teacher.
A teacher is not a preacher. A preacher is not a teacher.
A teacher can only be a teacher.
A teacher cannot be a preacher.
A preacher will not be a teacher. That I say solemnly."

Truth & Oneness

PART THREE—AFFIRMATION FOR SELF-LOVE

Sit straight in a cross-legged position.

EYES: Closed.

1. Hold hands with your neighbors. Chant: ***God and Me, Me and God, are One***. If what you chant is true, press the hands. If not, do not. The other person will know if you have spoken the truth or if you are a liar. Continue for **11 to 31 minutes**.

TO END: Adjust your shoulders, raising and stretching out your right arm, then the left.

Deeply inhale and, without disconnecting the hands, very calmly relax, stretching the spine with one long complete exhale. Then let go of the hands and stretch your body:

    a) raise both arms straight up, twist left and right;

    b) bring both knees to your chest, lock them with the hands and press hard toward yourself;

    c) extend the legs straight forward. Feel happy and relax.

continued on next page

Truth & Oneness

2. Sit straight in a cross-legged position.

POSITION A: Raise both arms straight up over the head and hold your hands in Sarab Gyan Mudra—fingers interlocked with the index fingers together pointing up and thumbs crossed. Eyes are closed. Rhythmically chant in a monotone from the navel:

Whaa-hay Hoo, Whaa-hay Gu-roo

Emphasize *Hoo* and *Roo* and extend the second *Hay* longer than the first.

POSITION B: Bring both hands to shoulder level with the elbows relaxed down, palms facing forward, and rhythmically chant in a monotone:

Raa Raa Raa Raa Raa, Maa Maa Maa Maa Maa,
 Laa Laa Laa Laa Laa, Saa Saa Saa Saa Saa

With emphasis on the last ...*Raa* ...*Maa* ...*Laa* ...*Saa.*
Alternate position A and B three times. Relax.

3. Chant the *Ek Aacharee Chand shabd*: ***Ajai, Alai.*** (The version by Gurushabd Singh and Sarab Shakti Kaur was used in class). Continue for **11 minutes**. End by singing the Long Time Sun song, ending with three long *Sat Nam*'s.

4. Quickly stand up and sit down **4-6 times**. Dance with Bangra music for **3 minutes**.

TO END: Inhale, exhale, sit down and relax.

Group Meditation With Punjabi Drums

1. The whole group stands up and dances to *Punjabi Drums* by Matamandir Singh. Let your whole body move in a rhythmical way.

TIME: Continue for **11 minutes**.

2. Sit straight in Easy Pose, eyes focused at the tip of the nose. Allow your breath to become automatically very slow and deep by becoming present and alert. As your breath becomes calm and steady, go into absolute deep silence. Go deep within yourself. Keep control of your mind. Be steady and firm. Enjoy the rhythm of stillness. Allow stillness and silence to be in every fiber of your being. You may use the mental guidance of the following narrative of Yogi Bhajan:

Now we get peaceful. We close our eyes, going through our self. You have to give something to receive. Personally what you have to give yourself is the chance to be silent. Do you know the beauty? You just close your eyes and look within yourself, so that you can look all around. Silence is the language of all languages. Make it possible so that we can be serene. Still your body, every fiber of it.

Now fiber by fiber, you rejoice in your body. Concentrate on every part of it, every pore of it. Feel it. With all the strength, with all the knowledge, with all the feelings if you can feel your own body you have achieved something unique. Because you are you, without you there is nothing. The entire universe around you is also within you. If you can feel yourself, from that you can feel everything. Concentrate and go deep into every part of your self.

Start it from the very tip of the toes up to the top ends up your hair. Do an absolute survey. Make it a very conscious survey. Do it with self-dignity. Explore every fiber of you. Deep in you is the creative power of God, it is the Generating power, Organizing power and the Destroying power, all centered in you. Try to locate that center. If you can help yourself you can help the whole world.

Deep in you is the rhythm of your life. Whether you are old or young, a woman or a man, if you cannot listen to this rhythm you have not yet found the happiness of life. Try to concentrate and see this energy, which is the left part of your body and right part of your body interchanging all the time.

Now open your eyes, and take your hands and rub them as fast as you can.

TIME: Continue for **31 minutes**.

TO END: Inhale deep, hold the breath, and pull the navel in with all your strength. Exhale. Repeat 2 more times. On the last breath, inhale completely, pull the navel in, and synchronize every fiber of your body. Relax.

Healing the Wounds of Love—
with Sacred Geometry

This meditation can be done alone (*see pages 40-41*) or recited with a group. There is a very powerful way to do it in a large group, using a specific geometry. It is a very old secret of *gurmat*—the way of living given by the Sikh masters. The essence of this is to use the *Naad* of this Shabd to reshape the electromagnetic aura to reflect the perfect relationship within one's Self and with the Infinite/Soul that is ultimate love.

When Yogi Bhajan gave this class he was radiant and full of the love he spoke about. In that spirit, he shared an ideal way to chant this in a group to amplify its effect by building a strong aura and psycho-electromagnetic field. He called this way of chanting Reactive Unison Communication. This way, each person's projection is amplified thousands of times by everyone else's, powerful enough to heal the wounds of many lifetimes.

MANTRA: *Mera Man Lochai shabd* from Shabd Hazaray. The words for this meditation are on page 40.
(*Healing the Wounds of Love* recording by Guru Raj Kaur was created for this meditation.)

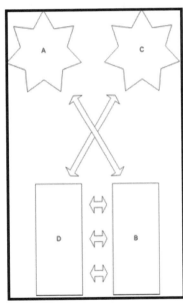

**Sacred Geometry of
Shabd Hazaray Meditation**

GROUP EXPERIENCE: Split the group into two groups (D + B) facing each other. No need for lines, but everyone sits straight and faces the other group. Put two smaller groups (A + C) in front, seated at 60° angles to each other. Ideally they are musicians who can play the Shabd.

- Begin with A + B (diagonal from each other) chanting the *Aad Sach* mantra, then the first letter of Shabd Hazaray together as the others listen.
- Then, groups C + D chant the *Aad Sach* mantra with the second letter.
- Switch again, with A + B chanting the *Aad Sach* mantra with the third letter
- Switch again, with C + D chanting the *Aad Sach* mantra with the fourth letter
- Then, everyone (A + B + C + D) chants the *Aad Sach* mantra 4 times after letter 4.

Continue this pattern through the entire shabd repeating the cycle **11 times**.

TIME: As long as it takes to complete the 11 cycles. (approximately 45 minutes.)

TO END: After you finish establishing this powerful field of energy, sit perfectly still and listen to the shabd sung in a very etheric manner for **15-20 minutes**.

COMMENTS

Even if you are unfamiliar with this shabd, reading it along with the sounds or hearing and repeating as you hear is very effective. Very quickly the rhythm and music will penetrate your cells in the primal language of sound.

During the group chanting, your mind and subconscious let go of many pains and find the sensitive, aware presence and confidence of the soul. As you listen in a deep state of shuniya, the element of ether opens the mind and aura to allow new perceptions and new actions. The root that you placed deep into your soul reaches out to a new relationship and blooms.

Group Solidarity Meditation

Sit as a group in a circle, each person in Easy Pose.

MUDRA: Interlock arms with the person on either side of you.

EYES: Eyes focus on the tip of the nose.

BREATH: Inhale through the nose silently in 4 segments:

> Turn head to left shoulder and mentally chant **Saa** as you inhale one part of the breath.
>
> Turn head to right shoulder and mentally chant **Taa** as you inhale 1/4 more
>
> Turn head to left shoulder mentally chant **Naa** as you inhale 1/4 more.
>
> Turn head to right shoulder and mentally chant **Maa** as you complete the last 1/4 inhale.
>
> Then face the head forward at the center line of the body and chant aloud together on the exhale:

Whaa-hay Guroo, Whaa-hay Guroo, Whaa-hay, Whaa-hay, Whaa-hay Guroo

Begin the four-part segmented breath again, and chant on the exhale.

TIME: Continue for **11 minutes**.

TO END: Inhale and exhale, and repeat this twice more, then relax.

COMMENTS

This meditation builds a group aura; you will even be willing to die for each other.

Mahan Jaap

The group sits attentively in Easy Pose in a meditative posture, and meditates at the Brow Point, with eyes closed. It is not necessary for the group to sit in a circle, though you may.

MANTRA: The group begins chanting the Panj Shabd all together for approximately **1 minute**.

Saa Taa Naa Maa

Inhale, exhale. The teacher then begins the first cycle alone. Someone else immediately picks up the chant as the first person ends. It is important to maintain the rhythm. Anyone can pick up the chant at any time; it does not move in a sequential order, nor does it move around the circle or room. Best to maintain a brisk rhythm, making each cycle 2 1/2 to 3 seconds.

TIME: Variable. Go with the flow.

TO END: The leader will chant with everyone at once for **2 minutes**. Then inhale, and relax.

COMMENTS

You can repeat as many times as you like as an individual. The individual will become sensitized on a new level so that he or she will respond to the energy in the group. Each person is a part of the greater energy balance. You will chant in response and resonance to the shift of the total group energy. If it is your turn then chant. If not, pass. You will sense when the energy comes to you to fill, complete or contribute. Ultimately, the individual activity merges with the group activity, with no difference between them, since it is the energy focus of the group that shifts and causes someone to chant. Some may chant more than one time, many times, periodically, not periodically, or even not at all. More than one person might chant together, too. That is okay. It requires stillness and a very delicate and sublime sensitivity.

Healing Ring of Tantra

Eleven or more people sit in a circle, in any comfortable, cross-legged position. Form an unbroken circle by holding hands.*

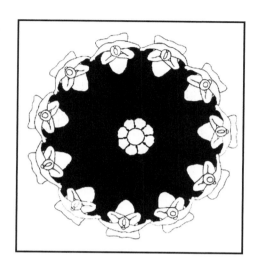

EYES: The eyes are closed.

MANTRA: The mantra goes around the circle, with each person taking a turn to powerfully call out the mantra in a monotone, answered by all the members of the circle:

Whaa-Hay Guroo

Whaa and *Hay* each have 1 beat, and *Gu-roo* has 2 beats. The caller then says *Sat Naam* softly, and the person sitting to the left of the caller becomes the next caller. (The silent Sat Naam should not effect the rhythm.) The chant continues in a clockwise direction around the circle, maintaining a constant rhythm.

BREATH PATTERN: Inhale as the mantra is being chanted by a caller; exhale as you chant the mantra in response.

TIME: Practice for at least **11 minutes**, and not longer than **31 minutes**.

COMMENTS

The healing ring can be used to generate and direct tremendous healing energy toward any person: a member of the circle, someone at a far distance, or someone located in the center of the circle. The participants should focus their minds to listen, and let themselves be filled with the sound, acutely tuning into the call, and then answering.

SPIRAL FORMAT. Another way to do this meditation is with the participants seated in a spiral. Participants join hands, alternately facing in opposite directions. (The left hand of one person will hold the left hand of the person to their left; right hand to right hand of person to their right.) If there are people of both genders, the seating in the spiral should alternate between male and female. Same gender individuals can complete the outer tail of the spiral. The person seated in the center of the spiral, if possible, should be a woman. The person seated in the center and the one in the outermost position of the spiral should hold the palms of each of their free hands facing up, to connect with the Infinite.

The chanting begins with the person seated in the center, and proceeds to the next person in the spiral, until the outermost person chants. Then the chanting proceeds back to the center person.

An effective way to do this is to, if possible, have a musician (guitar, harmonium, drum), which helps to keep the beat and set a simple melody and rhythm.

*This meditation in either format is only to be done on the days of the Full Moon, New Moon, and eleventh day of the New Moon, with a minimum of eleven people. During the meditation, the ring must never be broken for any reason.

Creating a Group Sound Current
Hearing the Subtle Interplay of Naad

There is a very enjoyable form of music where you sing in "rounds," to create and enjoy a group sound. The same lyric is sung by different parts of a larger group, each part starting the same words at a different point. Often the music is varied a bit to harmonize.

Yogi Bhajan led us in many examples of this. We will use the mantra *Sa Ta Na Ma.* Chanting together creates a ring of sound within a group which is more magnificent than one person chanting alone. The ability of the group to listen and adjust their frequencies to work together in harmony, tone and tempo create a special effect and beauty. It is a practice of listening to the universal *Naad.* You will also hear "overtones." These sound like tones that do not belong to any one person or have any one locality. Yogis would meditate on these to train the mind to listen to the etheric sounds and to stimulate the higher centers.

Everyone chant in rounds for **11 minutes**.

CHAPTER NINE

CRISIS KIT

SERVING THE INFINITE

Crossing the Crisis

"You have the right to create harmony and you have the right to create crisis, nobody creates them for you. You create them, you will live with them, and you will bury yourself with them. There is just one way to get out, and that is to grow. Grow consciously—that is the one chance we all have." 1

–Yogi Bhajan

As we approach the Aquarian Age, we have to cultivate the wisdom to avoid crisis where possible, and the tools to address it effectively where necessary. These meditations are your tool kit, providing long-term solutions as well as brief interludes to break the psychic space that holds us in crisis. They are, in short, lullabies for the soul. These meditations are gatkas, short, precise ways to effectively cut through the neurosis and become grounded, steady and at ease.

Most people, especially in the Western World, freak out when a crisis arises. Here in the United States it seems the smaller the issue the greater the reaction. Meanwhile, the Aquarian Age demands a shift in consciousness, demands that we reach out to one another when we're in crisis, demands that we create unity in the face of tragedy. We see the shift happening every day: in the face of a financial breakdown, people have created volunteer pools to trade skills until work comes their way; in the face of danger and imminent death, we see Chilean miners creating a group consciousness that would sustain them for 69 days underground; in the face of increasing violence, we see women continue to fight for education and opportunity for their daughters and their sisters all around the world. In this way, we see that our virtues and our values carry us across any short-term challenges. When we think of others, when we are inspired to be selfless, when we grow beyond the

boundaries of self, then the crisis falls away and we create an environment of solutions.

"Every victory has a price. Every defeat has a pain; therefore, don't let your ego play an unnecessary role. The best is to accept the Will of God—and the Will of God is what is best for all, not what is best for you. That is the only difference. What is best for you is best for you. It is not the Will of God; it is your will. If you sacrifice your will to the Divine Will, then you wish good for all and you shall be the best. That is the way to cross the crisis."2

–Yogi Bhajan

When we can maintain an attitude of Sahej and transcend the negativity through ease, peace of mind, and tranquility; when we can live as *Jiwan Mukt*, dead while alive, we hold the keys to crossing the crises in our lives and supporting others in crossing their own. Cultivate the strength to sacrifice, project your radiance in all you do, and be alert and steady ready to face the crisis and deliver yourself, and all those with you, safely to the other side.

In the days, weeks and years to come, people will come to you looking for help, know these meditations by heart, or keep them close by so that you can share them with those who need a way to shift their consciousness—now!

Keeping You Steady & on the Path

Sit straight in Easy Pose.

MUDRA: Place the right palm on the back of the left hand. Both palms face down in front of your torso at the level of the Heart Center.

EYES: Eyes are focused at the tip of the nose or 1/10th open.

MANTRA: Chant the following 3 times on a single breath.

Ha-ree naam sat naam ha-ree naam ha-ree
Ha-ree naam sat naam sat naam ha-ree

TIME: Continue for **31 minutes**.

COMMENTS

This is a mantra and meditation that keeps you on the path. This meditation will integrate your time and how your internal self deals with all the projections through time. In the midst of all thoughts, emotions, and commotion, this Aspect keeps you on the path. When balanced, you can say, and mean, "All this life is Your gift. The pain and tragedy is as sweet as nectar." You are alert to any positive or negative impact that can sway you from your essential path. You can find the silver lining in any cloud. You defend by awareness, not by reaction or threat. You guide your project between all the interests that would interfere or stop it. You pass the challenges and sail toward fulfillment.

Balancing Behavior & Impulse

PART ONE
Sit in Easy Pose with a straight spine.

MUDRA: Place the hands at the level of the mouth. Cup the hands slightly while keeping the fingers straight. Bend the hands at the wrist so that the right hand fingers point down while the left hand fingers point up. The hands do not touch.

EYES: Close the eyes and mentally look through the forehead.

TIME: **11 minutes.**

PART TWO
Same posture and focus, but with hand positions reversed: the right hand fingers point up while the left hand fingers point down and repeat.

TIME: **11 minutes.**

COMMENTS
This kriya balances your energy flow, and your behavior comes less from impulse, and more from the appropriate need of the moment.

Meditation for Stress & Sudden Shock

Sit in an Easy Pose, with a light jalandhar bandh.

MUDRA: Relax the arms down with the elbows bent. Draw the forearms in toward each other until the hands meet in front of the body about 1 inch (2.5 cm) above the navel. Place the palms up, and rest the right hand in the palm of the left hand. Place the thumbtips together, and pull the thumbs toward the body.

EYES: Look at the tip of the nose, the Lotus Point.

BREATH: Deeply inhale and completely exhale as you chant the mantra.

MANTRA: Chant the mantra 3 times. The entire mantra must be chanted on only one breath. Use the tip of the tongue to pronounce each word exactly, and chant in a monotone. The rhythm must also be exact.

Sat Naam Sat Naam Sat Naam Sat Naam
Sat Naam Sat Naam Whaa-hay Guroo

TIME: Begin with **11 minutes** and slowly build up to **31 minutes**.

TO END: Inhale and completely exhale 5 times. Then deeply inhale, hold the breath and stretch the arms up over the head as high as possible. Stretch with every ounce that you can muster. Exhale and relax down. Repeat twice.

COMMENTS

This meditation balances the left hemisphere of the brain with the base of the right hemisphere. This enables the brain to maintain its equilibrium under stress or the weight of a sudden shock. It also keeps the nerves from being shattered under those circumstances.

Meditation for a Calm Mind & Strong Nerves

Sit with a straight spine.

MUDRA: Hold the right hand at ear level with the thumb tip and Sun (ring) finger touching (fingernails don't touch). Place the left hand in the lap with the thumb tip and the Mercury (pinkie) finger touching.

Females reverse the position: The left hand has thumb and ring finger touching with the hand at ear level, and the right hand is in the lap with the thumb and little finger touching.

EYES: The eyes are one-tenth open.

BREATH: Breathe long and deep with a relaxed, rhythmic breath.

TIME: You can practice this meditation anywhere, starting with **11 minutes** and working up to **31 minutes**.

TO END: Inhale deeply, open the fingers, raise the hands and shake them rapidly for several minutes. Relax.

COMMENTS

Practice this meditation to gain a calm mind and strong nerves. It will help protect you from irrationality.

Get Stable—Anywhere

Sit anywhere, any place.

MUDRA & MOVEMENT: Hold the left hand up as though to clap. With the Jupiter (index) and Saturn (middle) fingers of the right hand, slowly and with strong pressure, walk up the center of the left palm to the very tips of the ring and middle fingers. The left fingers should give in—bend a little under the pressure, and it should hurt. Walk up and down the palm.

EYES: The eyes are one-tenth open.

TIME: **3-11 minutes**.

COMMENTS

This meditation neutralizes the central part of the brain and makes you sharp-witted. It is the answer to abnormal conditions we don't understand. Sit with a straight spine.

Bringing Mental Balance

Sit with a straight spine.

MUDRA: Interlace the fingers with the palms facing up; fingers point up at a gentle 60° angle; thumbs are straight. Hold the inverted Venus Lock at the solar plexus.

EYES: The eyes are one-tenth open.

MANTRA: Chant the Guru Gaitri Mantra:

Gobinday, Mukanday, Udaaray, Apaaray,
Hareeang, Kareeang, Nirnaamay, Akaama

These are the eight aspects of God:
    Sustainer, Liberator, Enlightener, Infinite,
    Destroyer, Creator, Nameless, Desireless.

It should totally turn into a sound current. Chant as fast as possible so that the words are indistinguishable.

TIME: Start with **11 minutes** and over time build up to **31 minutes**.

COMMENTS

When you're at your wits' end, when you don't know what to do, when nothing else works, this meditation does!

This is one of five meditations given specifically "to prepare for the gray period of the planet and to bring mental balance."

Three Kriyas to Eliminate Tension & Stress

Relaxing Buddha

A relaxing pose that will release tension and stress in just 11 minutes. Sit in Easy Pose. Your right elbow is bent and resting on the right knee. Lean the right cheekbone on the palm of the right hand with the fingers loosely covering the right half of the forehead. Close your eyes and just relax. This pose will put pressure on your liver, so just relax and let the body adjust to it. If you want to really relax, play the Guru Ram Das Lullaby as you do this meditation. **11 minutes**.

A most powerful combination against stress is to do the Relaxing Buddha meditation followed by 31 minutes of One Minute Breath (inhale 20 seconds, hold 20 seconds, and exhale 20 seconds). It will bring you to a state of calmness that will win the game of life. Normally there is so much tension in life that we are all numb. We miss opportunities through a lack of sensitivity.

Experiencing the Jupiter Energy

Sit in Easy Pose.

Left hand mudra: The Saturn (middle) finger crosses over the back of the Jupiter (index) finger. The other two fingers are closed and locked down with the thumb. The back of the left hand rests on the left knee.

Right hand mudra: The Jupiter (index) finger extends straight up and the other fingers are closed and locked down with the thumb. Right elbow is bent and the right hand is about chin level. Close your eyes, relax, and quickly move the Jupiter finger around in a circle. Only the Jupiter finger moves.

Concentrate on moving the Jupiter finger. Listen to *Ang Sang Wahe Guru* recording by Nirinjan Kaur. **11 minutes**.

TO END: Inhale, keep the finger moving, and tighten all the muscles of the body as you hold the breath for 10 seconds. Exhale and repeat two more times.

This meditation can release tension and call in the Jupiter energy of prosperity and expansion.

Three Kriyas to Eliminate Tension & Stress

Getting Rid of Tension So You Can Live

Sit in Easy Pose.

Extend your arms out and down with the palms up. Circle your extended arms inward and upward and continue around to complete the circle. Really push hard as you move upward.
3 minutes.

TO END: Inhale deeply and relax.

Earthquake Meditation
For When You've Lost Your Ground

Sit straight in a meditative posture.

MUDRA: Slightly cup your left hand and hold it over the left ear. Hold the left arm in front of you so that the upper arm is parallel to the ground. Bring your right hand into a fist up by your ear, Conch Mudra.

EYES: Eyes are focused on the tip of the nose.

MANTRA: Strike the side of your head with your left hand in time with the mantra *Saa Taa Naa Maa* sung in the traditional way.

TIME: **11-31 minutes.**

COMMENTS

The magnetic relationship of the two hemispheres of the brain is readjusted with this meditation. This meditation can readjust your electromagnetic field after an earthquake or other trauma.

CHAPTER TEN

HEAL YOURSELF &
HEAL THE WORLD

SERVING THE INFINITE

Grow & Glow

"Be the change you want to see."
–Mahatma Gandhi

The New Age has brought with it a plethora of healing modalities along with a completely new perspective and syntax around the notion of wellness and illness. We all want to be able to make a difference; we all have the desire to help. But as with most things, we need to begin at home. I'm reminded of the adage, "physician heal thyself." Have we done the essential groundwork on ourselves first? Health comes from the Indo-European word, kailo, meaning whole, in-tact, uninjured; it then moved into the Greek and Latin roots hælþ and sol, which came to mean wholeness, being whole, sound or well. So before we can heal others, we must first be whole ourselves. We need to reach a state of integrity—completeness—before we can truly begin the work of healing others. How do we get there? *Ek Ong Kar Sat Gurprasaad*—Guru's Grace—along with a little work of our own.

Yogi Bhajan often said that as Teachers of the Aquar-ian Age we would also serve as healers, leaders and sages: "Your presence should be a healing." What does it mean to heal as a Teacher? What does it mean to have a radiance that elevates people just by entering the room? What does it take to maintain that presence?

Yogi Bhajan gave us so many tools to work with. There are meditations for addiction and compulsive behavior; there are pranayam practices to charge the hands as a healer; there are kriyas for self-healing; there are recipes and herbs to support the physical body and so much more. We've included a handful of the hundreds of practices he gave here; becoming familiar with these tools will surely support your students, but what is at the heart of it all? Our own presence and projection as Teachers.

As Teachers, we rely upon the power of prayer and the connection to the Golden Chain, allowing the hand of Guru Ram Das to work. Can we make a difference and intervene where necessary? Sure. But in the end, our presence, our projection, and our prayer are what ultimately carry people through whatever obstacles they find in their way—and it's Guru Ram Das who removes them—not us. Takes the pressure off, doesn't it?

People heal themselves. People allow the process, the transformation, to take hold or not. We simply get to witness it—with no small amount of reverence and hu-mility—and recognize the incredible courage it takes to let things go and cultivate new habits that serve their soul and their spirits.

As someone in the course of continual transforma-tion, we recognize the gift that is found in the Teach-ings of Yogi Bhajan. A simple 5-minute pranayam can change the course of our day. An 11-minute practice of *Raa Maa Daa Saa*, when practiced with an intention to heal ourselves and others, can change the way we see the world. As practitioners, we have access to the energy of the Kundalini, which can transform us in the space of one breath or create the psychic heat over days and weeks and months and years to purify ourselves and, in time, find the truest healing—*Sat Nam*—our own identity.

Grow & Glow

"It is the responsibility of all of us to grow. We must start healing the world, which is going to come at us, so this is the time to grow. And with that we grow and glow, hail and heal, and keep going. Stop this, 'I have cough, I'm this, I'm that'; if you want to find a sick man, look no more, I'm worse than all you can know. There's not a single thing that is not wrong with me, but however wrong is wrong, sing a song: "I'm wrong, wrong is wrong, there's nothing wrong; get going; keep going," something like that. The word, Keep up!, is the most well-coined word. Count all your curses and say, 'curses you are dead, I'm keeping up.' That's all you need. It's a simple psychological transformation, one word, Keep Up!, *Cherdi Kala.*

–Yogi Bhajan[1]

As Teachers, we have the opportunity to heal ourselves and truly heal the world. Begin today and bless every tomorrow.

Healing Pranayams: Self-Care Breath

Sit comfortably in a meditative posture.

MUDRA: Place the hands crossed over the Heart Center, right over left. Open the mouth and form a circle that is tight and precise—a boar's mouth.

EYES: Close your eyes and sense the area under your palms.

BREATH: Breathe a steady, powerful Cannon Breath through the mouth. Let your mind focus on the mouth ring and shape the breath into a ring.

TIME: **5 minutes**.

TO END: Inhale and hold the breath. Relax the mouth. Mentally repeat:
"I am beautiful, I am innocent, I am innocent, I am beautiful."
Exhale through the nose. Do this a total of five times. Then relax.

COMMENTS

Self-care breath increases inner energy and strength, boosts the immune system, and cleanses the body.

Healing Pranayams: Breath of Ten
Meditation to Become Disease-Free

Sit in Easy Pose with a straight spine. Bring your hands into a clapping position in front of you. Your hands will move in and out as if you were clapping, but don't let the hands touch. When your hands are about 12 inches apart, stop the inward motion and start moving them outward. Move slowly and rhythmically. Concentrate on the energy that you feel between the palms of your hands.

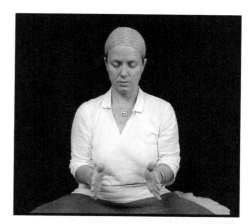

The breath is timed with the movement of the hands.

> Inhale in five strokes through the nose.
> Exhale in five strokes through the mouth.

Each stroke of the breath is one clapping motion. Do not break the rhythm of the movement or the breath.

TIME: **11 minutes**.

TO END: Inhale deeply and press your hands against your face as hard as you can while holding the breath in. 20 seconds. Exhale. Inhale deeply and press your hands strongly against your Heart Center while holding your breath. 20 seconds. Exhale. Inhale deeply and press your hands hard against your Navel Point while holding your breath. 20 seconds. Exhale and relax.

COMMENTS

"Your value is in your breath of life. Enhance your capacity." The Breath of Ten is a complete breath in the line of Breath of Fire. It can give you a disease-free body, clear, meditative mind and intuition, but it requires practice. This is magnetic energy therapy. The exercise triggers the command center to wake up your immune system. It puts all the chakras in rhythm. The body's resources are invoked to heal you.

Self-Care Kriya

When Yogi Bhajan originally taught this at Khalsa Women's Training Camp, he had the women start with a quick warm up: two rounds of the Har Aerobic Kriya. *(This kriya can be found in Transformation Volume 1, Mastering the Self. Also in I Am a Woman.)*

1. Stand up and wrap the arms around the chest crossing in the front. Hands are hugging the back, just under the rib cage. Hold the rib cage as tight as you can. Begin jumping slightly as legs are lifted alternately in front of the body, as if dancing and kicking the legs forward. It is called "walking the miracle mile."
3 1/2 minutes.

2. Same basic exercise as above but after kicking first one leg and then the other you will bend forward and touch your toes. Then pop back up and kick your legs forward again. Continue alternating both movements.
2 minutes.

3. Sitting on the heels, clasp the hands together and rest them on the top of your head. Rotate your torso around in a circle, moving from the waist. This will release toxins from your cells that can eventually block your blood flow. **1 minute.**

Self-Care Kriya

4. Still sitting on your heels, press the palms of your hands just under the cheekbones and lift. It will be the Venus Mound of your palm pressing up under the cheekbones and should be enough pressure to prevent any speech. Inhale through pursed lips, take deep drinks of air and exhale powerfully through the nose. **2 minutes.**

5. Sitting in Easy Pose and using the same breath pattern as in Exercise 4, place your hands on the knees and bend at the waist from side to side. Inhale deeply on one side and exhale deeply on the other side. **2 minutes.**

6. Lie down flat on your back, with your arms by your side and go to sleep for one hour. Play Singh Kaur's recording of *Rakhe Rakhanhar*. Relax and let yourself go. **1 hour.**
This music has 8 beats like your heartbeat. You must be able to hypnotize yourself into going to sleep.

COMMENTS
"A yogi must be in control of their sleep and should be able to turn on the sleep button at any time. It is called self-hypnosis."
                                                            - Yogi Bhajan

Relieve, Relax, Recharge

1. Sitting in a comfortable position, like Easy Pose, place the palms on the temples. Breathe long and deep. As you inhale, press the temples with the hands. As you exhale, release the pressure. Continue pressing and releasing the temples with your breath. **4 minutes.**

2. Still seated, take both hands and wrap them around the sides of your neck. As you inhale, apply pressure to the neck. As you exhale, release the pressure. **3 minutes.**

3. Place the hands on the waist. The thumbs will be on the back and fingers around the front. Thumbs will be at the kidney area and your fingers will be at the liver/ gall bladder and spleen area. Apply pressure with the hands as you inhale and release the pressure as you exhale. **2 minutes.**

4. Make fists of your hands and rhythmically pound the upper chest, above the breasts. This is the lymph area you are stimulating and circulating. You will breathe as you strike so it will become a powerful Breath of Fire. **2 minutes.**

5. Pound the Navel Point with your fists. Breath of Fire. **1 1/2 minutes.**

6. Pound the inner, upper thigh with your fists. Continue with strong Breath of Fire. **1 minute.**

Relieve, Relax, Recharge

7. Pound the lower sides of your back in the kidney area. Moderate the pressure of the pounding— not very hard, just enough to get it stimulated. Continue with Breath of Fire. **1 minute**.

8. Come into Frog Pose, squatting down with the heels touching, off the ground, feet turned slightly outward. Spread the knees wide, have arms in between the spread knees. Place fingertips on the ground. Straighten the spine as much as possible in this squatting position. Inhale, keeping the heels off the ground, extend up by straightening your legs and lifting the hips. Use a very strong breath, inhaling up and exhaling down. **21 repetitions**.

9. Come standing straight and raise the arms up over the head. Hands are locked together in Venus Lock. Squat down into Crow Pose and then raise yourself back into the standing position. Hands stay overhead throughout the exercise. **41 repetitions**.

10. Come sitting down in Easy Pose and clasp the hands behind the neck. Bring your forehead to the ground and then raise yourself back up. Inhale up, exhale down. **21 repetitions**.

continued on next page

Relieve, Relax, Recharge

11. Sit in Easy Pose and cross your arms in front of your chest with hands locked on the shoulders. Bend at the waist from the left to right. Inhale down, exhale up to center.
21 repetitions.

12. Lie down flat on the back with hands at your sides. Put the heels together and raise the legs up to a 90 degree angle as you inhale. Bring the legs back down on the exhale.
42 repetitions.

13. Lower the legs down and lie flat on your back with the arms by your sides. Hypnotize yourself to fall into a long, deep sleep listening to a recording of *Rakhe Rakhanhaar*. **1 hour.**

COMMENTS
Rakhe Rakhanhaar is the most powerful prayer in the combination of sound and words. With it, there is nothing between God and man.

Renew Your Rhythms & Invite Prosperity

Sit in Easy Pose with a straight spine.

MUDRA: Stretch your arms out to the sides with the palms down. On each hand, touch your thumb to the mound under the Mercury (pinkie) finger. Close your fist around the thumb. Keep the elbows straight as you revolve your arms and fists backwards in 18" circles. Move quickly.
The circles must be 18" wide for this movement to be effective.

BREATH: Breathe like a cobra, with a hissing breath through the nose.

MUSIC & RHYTHM: *Tantric Har* by Simran Kaur has the proper rhythm and can be used with this meditation.

TIME: **11 minutes**.

TO END: Inhale deeply, expand the rib cage, hold the breath for 8 seconds and exhale powerfully, with Cannon Breath. Repeat this sequence twice more.

COMMENTS

This meditation, done with the thumb touching the mound of Mercury, will communicate to every organ of the body to re-organize and regulate itself. It is calming and, if practiced for 120 days, will put everything in the body in rhythm. It can help menopausal problems, glandular system problems, and regulate any part of the body that needs regulation.

Variations: You can achieve different results with different mudras.
     If the thumb is on the mound of the Sun (ring) finger, this meditation will give you energy and will fight disease.
     If the thumb is on the mound of the Saturn (middle) finger, it will give you purity and the experience of ecstasy.
     If the Jupiter finger is extended, with the thumb touching the side of the Jupiter (index) finger and all the other fingers are closed, it will give you wisdom.

One kriya, experienced through sincere practice, without stress, in an attitude of surrender, is enough to give profound health to your body and mind. That health is essential for awareness. It is the first word in our motto: "Healthy, Happy and Holy." When the glands and nerves function well then they help you toward a realization of your spirit. Living without the awareness Yogi Bhajan is describing produces stress. It is like trying to walk 100 miles using only one toe instead of both feet.
     "Just be healthy. Then just be happy and holy, if you are healthy. I survived my own stress from overworking and over-serving because I am a yogi. My mind is very bright, self-controlled, and my soul and consciousness are very much with me. But I tell you: the physical body does interfere if you are not healthy. I know all the preventative exercises and herbs. I give this to you because they are effective and you can know them, and practice them, enjoy and prosper." —Yogi Bhajan

Power of the Mind Over the Body

1. Stretch the entire body. Move. **30-60 seconds**.

2. Sit as if Lord Buddha has taken an incarnation in you. Put your elbows on the seventh rib. Your hands are cupped, fingers relaxed and slightly apart, palms up, about 30 degrees above parallel. Look at the tip of the nose. Make an O of your mouth and inhale and exhale long and deep through the mouth. You will start feeling your hands become heavier and heavier and heavier, that's your magnetic strength. Meditate on the breath. You are healing by the breath.
Music: *Sat Nam Wahe Guru*. Indian Version. **9 minutes**.

   a) Maintain the posture but begin pumping the navel with the breath. **2 minutes**.
The energy can be dispersed and blood circulation can be purified.

   b) Maintain the posture but relax the breath and breathe normally as you pump the navel vigorously. Pump the navel back and forth with powerful strength, your spine will move, so the spinal serum will start going up and the brain will become fresh. **1 minute**.
You are equalizing the energy, sending the healthy blood where it needs to go.

TO END: Inhale deeply, hold the breath for 10 seconds and and press the hands together in Prayer Pose. Press hard. Exhale. Repeat twice more, holding the breath, for 5 and then 10 seconds and then relax.

Power of the Mind Over the Body

3. Balance your arms so that the elbows are wide and the forearms are angled toward each other, parallel with the ground, hands palm down. Bounce the hands and shoulders gently, about 3-4 inches, as you pump the navel. Breathe through the O mouth. After a few minutes bring the hands, shoulders, breath and navel to dance in rhythm with the music: *Tantric Har*. **7 minutes.**

TO END: Inhale, hold for 15 seconds and stretch the arms above head in Prayer Pose. Stretch your hands and spine. Exhale. Repeat twice more, suspending the breath for 5 seconds. Final exhale—Cannon Breath out.

4. Sit straight. Interlace the fingers with the thumbs pointing up. Place the palms against the Heart Center. The forearms are parallel to the ground to create a balance with the Earth's magnetic field. Close the eyes. Breathe in deeply and suspend the breath. When you can't hold the breath any longer, exhale and repeat. **7–11 minutes.**

With self-hypnosis, direct your body's energy, the prana, to go and eat up the dead cells; eat up any negativity—mental, physical, or spiritual.

TO END: Inhale deeply and hold the breath for 15 seconds; press your hands hard against your chest and sqeeze your body. Cannon Breath exhale. Repeat twice more suspending the breath for 10 seconds each time. Relax.

COMMENTS

We are going to heal our glandular system... glands are the guardians of health . . . If you deal with the world from your spirit, from your soul, you will be prosperous, graceful and saintly. If you have a relationship with your body, with your glandular system, you will always be effective and great and jubilant.

Medical Meditation for Habituation

Sit in a comfortable pose. Straighten the spine and make sure the first six lower vertebrae are locked forward.

MUDRA & MOVEMENT: Make fists of both hands and extend the thumbs straight. Place the thumbs on the temples and find the niche where the thumbs just fit: the lower anterior portion of the frontal bone above the temporal-sphenoid suture.

Lock the back molars together and keep the lips closed. Vibrate the jaw muscles by alternating the pressure on the molars. A muscle will move in rhythm under the thumbs. Feel it massage the thumbs and apply a firm pressure with the fingers.

EYES: Keep the eyes closed and look toward the center of the eyes at the Brow Point. Silently vibrate the *Panj Shabd* mantra

Saa Taa Naa Maa

at the Brow Point in the same rhythm as the jaw muscles.

TIME: Continue **5 to 7 minutes**. With practice the time can be increased to **20 minutes** and ultimately to **31 minutes**.

COMMENTS

This meditation is one of a class of meditations that will become well-known to the future medical society. Meditation will be used to alleviate all kinds of mental and physical afflictions, but it may be a few hundred years before the new medical science will understand the effects of this kind of meditation well enough to delineate all its parameters in measurable factors.

The pressure exerted by the thumbs triggers a rhythmic reflex current into the central brain. This current activates the brain area directly underneath the stem of the pineal gland. It is an imbalance in this area that makes mental and physical addictions seemingly unbreakable.

In modern culture, the imbalance is pandemic. If we are not addicted to smoking, eating, drinking or drugs, then we are addicted subconsciously to acceptance, advancement, affection, emotional love, etc. All these lead us to insecure and neurotic behavior patterns.

The imbalance in this pineal area upsets the radiance of the pineal gland itself. It is this pulsating radiance that regulates the pituitary gland. Since the pituitary regulates the rest of the glandular system, the entire body and mind go out of balance. This meditation corrects the problem. It is excellent for everyone but particularly effective for rehabilitation efforts in drug dependence, mental illness, and phobic conditions.

Healing the Self

Sit in Easy Pose.

MUDRA: Arms are crossed, holding opposite shoulders. The left arm is over the right. The shoulders will carry the weight.

EYES: Closed.

MUSIC: Nirinjan Kaur's *Ang Sang Wahe Guru*
Sing with the tip of the tongue.

TIME: **31 minutes**.

Healing Imagery Meditation

Sit in Easy Pose with spine straight and relaxed.

MUDRA: Place the hands flat on the heart center, left under, right over.

EYES: Close the eyes.

MANTRA: Chant with the recording *Ang Sang Wahe Guru* by Nirinjan Kaur:

Ang Sang Whaa-Hay Guroo

MEDITATIVE VISUALIZATION:

Become fully present. Begin to focus on the Heart Center. This is a special center. It is called the *Hirday Chakra*. Your heart beats there. It is your pace of life. It has a strong electromagnetic field that eliminates itself into neutrality by its own rhythmical patterns.

Imagine that you are hypnotizing yourself. Become aware, alert, present and relaxed. Bring all of your attention to a very small, single tiny ray of platinum light. That ray is circling you. It is a very bright, distinct, white, shiny, platinum light. A circling ray that moves incredibly fast and smooth around your body.

Now make it two rays. Three. Four. Now a multitude that cover your entire being. There is a ray for every one of your ten trillion cells! You are light swirling and communicating between every cell, each with its own intelligence. They are moving faster, faster, with infinite fastness. Keep imagining deeper, and deeper and deeper.

Keep this imagery. It is *Wahe Guru* with every molecule and part of the molecule, every atom of you. This is the exact imagery of the mantra *Ang Sang Wahe Guru*. It is a *Panj Shabd* of five sounds that command the elements.

TIME: No specified time.

TO END: Inhale. Press on the Heart Center. Exhale. Relax.

Healing Imagery Meditation

COMMENTS
YOGI BHAJAN ON THE HEALING IMAGERY MEDITATION

When Yogi Bhajan gave the Healing Imagery Meditation he shared a guidance and a feeling about the process of being a teacher and progressing on the spiritual path.

"When you reach a consciousness like mine, and if you cannot handle it, it is like falling from the sky. The higher you are, the more dangerous it is. Spiritually be very slow, very firm and very consistent. That is Dharma.

If you fake it, you make it. I faked it that I am very happy to learn it. My environments were bad and I was handicapped, because I belonged to a very rich family, I was a spoiled brat. When I became a student this all went against me. Anything most weird, I was supposed to do. For instance:

"Bhajan?"

"Yes, sir?"

"For forty days, clean bathrooms."

"Yes, sir."

"And also supervise the kitchen."

"Yes, sir."

"And don't be late from college."

"Thank you, sir."

"And you know something? I promised the orphan school that I'll send them some food at lunch time. In your lunch time can you deliver that?"

"Yes, sir."

"Enough. But see it is done. And in the evening what are you doing?"

I said, "I do this, this, this." I have to explain everything.

"What time do you go to bed?"

"Eleven o'clock."

"Umm, too much. You sleep eleven to three?"

"Yeah."

"Tomorrow night we'll meet at eleven o'clock here."

I would go and we would have a wrestling match. About one o'clock we were asked to retire. At three o'clock we have to get up for sadhana. That's what all my riches got me. Everyone else was spared. They are poor guys. There's no kindness for me, because God has been kind already.

I'm very grateful to Almighty God who gave me the sense of that reality to go through it. Stay who you are. Be graceful with who you are. Then slowly and constantly, as each day progresses, add a spiritual touch to every day. That's why we read *Nitnem* (the daily prayers). That's why we read our *banis*. That's why we do our sadhana. That's why we do meditation.

Gradually and slowly we develop ourselves into that maturity, to that understanding, to that depth, to that firmness. So we can become radiant and our pleasantness starts working and the glow of our Arcline may cover our universe. That's the purpose of being a saint. It's very enjoyable, it's very satisfying. It's fun to be divine, and then to deal with divided people, divided identities. It gives you a totally different taste and enjoyment.

Satya Bandh

Sit in Easy Pose.

MUDRA: Palms face down with left hand 3-5 inches below the right hand. This distance must be exact. Hands are stacked right over left, with right hand parallel to ground immediately below the chin. Keep the chin in, and the chest out.

EYES: Eyes are open one millimeter.

BREATH: Slow, long deep breathing through the nose.

TIME: **11 minutes**.

MANTRA: To practice this meditation for healing, use the mantra:

Raa Maa Daa Saa (on inhale)
Saa Say So Hang (on exhale)

TO END: Inhale fully and exhale fully. Repeat the inhale and exhale cycle twice more. Relax.

TIME: The practice time for this meditation can gradually be extended to **31 minutes**.

COMMENTS
This kriya puts healing energy in the hands. It charges them.

APPENDIX

SHABD SHEETS

Guru Dev Mata

Guru Arjun Dev • Siri Guru Granth Sahib, page 250

Gurdev is the Divine Guru, the angelic, subtle, Transcendent Teacher

ਗੁਰਦੇਵ ਮਾਤਾ ਗੁਰਦੇਵ ਪਿਤਾ ਗੁਰਦੇਵ ਸੁਆਮੀ ਪਰਮੇਸੁਰਾ

Gurdev maata Gurdev pita. Gurdev swami parmeysura.

Gurdev is my Mother, Gurdev is my Father. Gurdev is my Transcendent Lord and Master

ਗੁਰਦੇਵ ਸਖਾ ਅਗਿਆਨ ਭੰਜਨੁ ਗੁਰਦੇਵ ਬੰਧਿਪ ਸਹੋਦਰਾ

Gurdev sakhaa agiaan bhanjan, Gurdev bandhap sahodraa

Gurdev is a friend and companion who dismisses the darkness of ignorance.
Such a relative which comes through every time.

ਗੁਰਦੇਵ ਦਾਤਾ ਹਰਿ ਨਾਮੁ ਉਪਦੇਸੈ ਗੁਰਦੇਵ ਮੰਤੁ ਨਿਰੋਧਰਾ

Gurdev daataa har naam updeysai, Gurdev mant nirodharaa

Gurdev is the Giver, the Teacher of the Lord's Name. Gurdev is the Mantra which never fails.

ਗੁਰਦੇਵ ਸਾਂਤਿ ਸਤਿ ਬੁਧਿ ਮੂਰਤਿ ਗੁਰਦੇਵ ਪਾਰਸ ਪਰਸ ਪਰਾ

Gurdev shaant sat budh moorat, Gurdev paaras paras paraa

Gurdev is the image of peace, truth and wisdom.
Gurdev is like the Philosopher's stone—whatever it touches, changes.

ਗੁਰਦੇਵ ਤੀਰਥੁ ਅੰਮ੍ਰਿਤ ਸਰੋਵਰੁ ਗੁਰ ਗਿਆਨ ਮਜਨੁ ਅਪਰੰਪਰਾ

Gurdev teerath amrit sarovar, Gur giaan majan aparanparaa

Gurdev is like a pilgrimage to a pool of nectar, whose uplifting knowledge is beyond, beyond, beyond.

ਗੁਰਦੇਵ ਕਰਤਾ ਸਭਿ ਪਾਪ ਹਰਤਾ ਗੁਰਦੇਵ ਪਤਿਤ ਪਵਿਤ ਕਰਾ

Gurdev kartaa sabh paap hartaa, Gurdev patit pavit karaa

Gurudev does everything and removes all sins, is honorable, and stands with purity.

ਗੁਰਦੇਵ ਆਦਿ ਜੁਗਾਦਿ ਜੁਗੁ ਜੁਗੁ ਗੁਰਦੇਵ ਮੰਤੁ ਹਰਿ ਜਪਿ ਉਧਰਾ

Gurdev aad jugaad jug jug, Gurdev mant har jap udharaa

Gurdev existed in the primal beginning, through all time, and always shall be.
Gurdev is the mantra of the Naam. Chanting it one is freed.

ਗੁਰਦੇਵ ਸੰਗਤਿ ਪ੍ਰਭ ਮੇਲਿ ਕਰਿ ਕਿਰਪਾ ਹਮ ਮੂੜ ਪਾਪੀ ਜਿਤੁ ਲਗਿ ਤਰਾ

Gurdev sangat prabh mel kar kirpaa. Ham moor paapee jit lag taraa

Gurdev creates the union between the congregation and God. Be merciful to me! That I may be with my Divine Guru. And though I make mistakes, holding on to you I am carried across.

ਗੁਰਦੇਵ ਸਤਿਗੁਰੁ ਪਾਰਬ੍ਰਹਮੁ ਪਰਮੇਸਰੁ ਗੁਰਦੇਵ ਨਾਨਕ ਹਰਿ ਨਮਸਕਰਾ ॥ 1 ॥

Gurdev satgur paarbrahm parmeshar, Gurdev naanak har namskaraa

Gurdev is the divinely true Teacher and true guide, the transcendent Lord.
Nanak bows in humble reverence to the Creative Guru.

Dhan Dhan Ram Das Gur

In Praise of Guru Ram Das • Siri Guru Granth Sahib, page 968

Dhan Dhan Ram Das Gur	*Praise, Praise Guru Ram Das!*
Jin siri-aa- tinai savaari-aa	*The Creator has adorned & embellished you!*
Pooree ho-ee karaamaat	*Perfect is the Miracle of your making*
Aap sirjanhaarai dhaari-aa	*The Creator has installed you on the Throne*
Sikhee atai sangatee	*Your Sikhs, and all people of consciousness bow*
Paarbrahm kar namasakaari-aa	*And revere you as a being of supreme consciousness*
Atal athaaho atoll too(n)	*You are unshakeable, unfathomable, immeasurable*
Tayraa ant na paaraavaari-aa	*Your extent is beyond all limits*
Jinee too(n) sayvi-aa bhaa-u kar	*Those who serve you with love*
Say tudh paar utaari-aa	*Are carried across the world-ocean by you*
Lab lobh kaam krodh moho	*The five passions of greed, attachment, lust, anger*
Maar kadhay tudh saparvaari-aa	*And ego have been transformed by you*
Dhaan so tayraa thaan hai	*Great and praised is your Realm*
Sach tayraa paisakaari-aa	*Truest of the true are Your bounties*
Nanak too(n) lehnaa too(n) hai	*You are Nanak, you are Angad,*
Gur Amar too(n) veechaari-aa	*And Guru Amar Das; I recognize this in you*
Gur dithaa taan man saadhaari-aa	*Seeing the Guru, my soul is comforted!*

ਧੰਨੁ ਧੰਨੁ ਰਾਮਦਾਸ ਗੁਰੁ ਜਿਨਿ ਸਿਰਿਆ ਤਿਨੈ ਸਵਾਰਿਆ

ਪੂਰੀ ਹੋਈ ਕਰਾਮਾਤਿ ਆਪਿ ਸਿਰਜਣਹਾਰੈ ਧਾਰਿਆ

ਸਿਖੀ ਅਤੈ ਸੰਗਤੀ ਪਾਰਬ੍ਰਹਮੁ ਕਰਿ ਨਮਸਕਾਰਿਆ

ਅਟਲੁ ਅਥਾਹੁ ਅਤੋਲੁ ਤੂ ਤੇਰਾ ਅੰਤੁ ਨ ਪਾਰਾਵਾਰਿਆ

ਜਿਨੀ ਤੂੰ ਸੇਵਿਆ ਭਾਉ ਕਰਿ ਸੇ ਤੁਧੁ ਪਾਰਿ ਉਤਾਰਿਆ

ਲਬੁ ਲੋਭੁ ਕਾਮੁ ਕਰੋਧੁ ਮੋਹੁ ਮਾਰਿ ਕਢੇ ਤੁਧੁ ਸਪਰਵਾਰਿਆ

ਧੰਨੁ ਸੁ ਤੇਰਾ ਥਾਨੁ ਹੈ ਸਚੁ ਤੇਰਾ ਪੈਸਕਾਰਿਆ

ਨਾਨਕੁ ਤੂ ਲਹਣਾ ਤੂ ਹੈ ਗੁਰੁ ਅਮਰੁ ਤੂ ਵੀਚਾਰਿਆ

ਗੁਰੁ ਡਿਠਾ ਤਾਂ ਮਨੁ ਸਾਧਾਰਿਆ

GLOSSARY

If you are a Kundalini Yogi, you may be familiar with many of the yoga terms used throughout this manual. If you haven't yet studied Kundalini Yoga as taught by Yogi Bhajan®, here is a brief introduction to terms. For best results in your practice, we encourage you to study with a KRI certified Kundalini Yoga teacher in your local community.

Adi Shakti: Literally means "Primal Power." Adi means "primal" or "first" and Shakti means "God's power manifested." The Adi Shakti has been worshipped for centuries in the Orient in the form of the goddess, and thus the female energy of Infinity is also referred to as Adi Shakti. Woman is seen as a manifestation of the Adi Shakti energy.

Age of Aquarius: The next in a succession of astrological ages each lasting roughly 2,000 years. Fully inaugurated in 2012, the Aquarian Age will witness a radical change in consciousness, human sensitivity, and technology. The central change of this new age emphasizes an increased sensitivity and evolution of our power of awareness and a new relationship to our mind.

Amrit Vela: Literally "ambrosial time." It is the 2-1/2 hours before the rising of the sun. During this special time you are most receptive to the soul; you can clear the subconscious of wrong habits and impulses; and you can connect with the teachers and saints from all traditions. It is the best time to perform sadhana (spiritual discipline).

Ang Sang Wahe Guru: "God exists in every part of me."

Aradhana: The second stage of spiritual discipline: sadhana, aradhana, prabhupati.

Arcline: One of 10 bodies of a human being. It is a thin bright arc, like a halo, that goes from ear to ear over the forehead near the normal hairline. It reflects the interaction of the soul of the person with its vital energy resources, and in it are written the potential, destiny, and health of the person. Women have a second Arcline from nipple to nipple.

Ardas: Prayer; the traditional formal prayer of the Sikhs.

Asana: Position, seat, yogic posture.

Ashram: A learning center for spiritual growth.

Ashtang Mantra: Most Kundalini Yoga Mantras are Ashtang Mantras, meaning they have 8 beats or 8 component parts in the sound current.

Aura: One of the 10 bodies, the aura is the radiant field of energy and consciousness that surrounds the physical body and which holds and organizes the seven centers of energy called chakras. Its strength, measured by brightness and radius, determines the vitality and integrity of a person.

Bana: Clothing which projects a particular consciousness.

Bani: Speech which projects a particular, elevated consciousness. Literally 'word'; refers to the Word of God contained in the Sikh Sacred writings.

Banis: The Sikh daily prayers.

Bhagvati (or Bhagauti): Creative Power of the Universe.

Bhakti: Self-purification. The devotional form of yoga.

Bandh: A body lock. There are three which make up the Maha Bandh or Great Lock: Jalandhar Bandh, Udiyana Bandh and Mulbandh.

Breath of Fire: One of the foundational breath techniques used in the practice of Kundalini Yoga. It accompanies many postures, and has numerous beneficial effects. It is important to master this breath so that it is done accurately and becomes automatic.

Chakra: The word connotes a wheel in action. It usually refers to the seven primary energy centers in the aura that align along the spine from the base to the top of the skull. Each chakra is a center of consciousness with a set of values, concerns, and powers of action associated with it.

Cherdi Kala. In high spirits. In the context of yoga, it refers literally to the moment when the Crown Chakra opens, the kundalini awakens, and you experience an expansion of spirit and a love for all brotherhood and sisterhood.

Dharma: A path of righteous living.

Easy Pose: This is a simple but stable yogic sitting posture. It is sitting cross-legged "tailor fashion," but with a yogic awareness of keeping the spine straight, with the lower spine slightly forward so the upper spine can stay straight.

Gatka: Indian martial art of sword fighting. Also refers to the use of mantra to cut through negativity or inertia and change the direction of the thought.

Golden Chain of Teachers or the Golden Link: Historically it is the long line of spiritual masters who have preceded us. Practically it is the subtle link between the consciousness of a student and the master, which has the power to guide and protect the energy of a teaching and its techniques. This link requires the student to put aside the ego and limitations and act in complete synchrony or devotion to the highest consciousness of the master and the teachings.

Gunas: The three conditions of matter: Satva (satvaa)—pure essence (saintliness), rajas (raajaas)—active, creative or initiating energy (imperial), and tamas (taamaas)—inertia or decay.

Gurbani: Word of the Guru. Refers particularly to the words from the Siri Guru Granth Sahib.

Gurmukh: Literally, one whose face is always turned toward the Guru, or one whose mouth always repeats the Guru's words; a perfectly devoted person.

Guru Mantra: Wahe Guru is the Guru Mantra in the Sikh Tradition. Refers to the bij or seed mantra given from teacher to student to elevate the consciousness.

Gyan Mudra: The most commonly used mudra for meditation. The tip of the thumb touches the tip of the Jupiter (index) finger. This stimulates knowledge, wisdom, and the power to compute. The energy of the index finger is associated with Jupiter, representing expansion. Its qualities are receptivity and calm.

Hukam: An order from the Guru.

Ida: One of the three major channels (nadis) for subtle energy in the body. It is associated with the flow of breath through the left nostril and represents the qualities of the moon—calmness, receptivity, coolness, and imagination. It is associated with the functions of the parasympathetic nervous system but is not identical to it nor derived from it.

Ishnan (ishnaan): A system of water therapy referred to in the West as "hydrotherapy," involving bathing in cold water to open the capillaries and flush the system, thus increasing the circulation and tonifying the glands and general health of the body.

Jaap Sahib: A prayer written by Guru Gobind Singh which gives one conscious awareness of one's grace; one of the banis, or daily prayer of the Sikhs.

Jalandar Bandh also called Neck Lock: This is the most basic of the locks. It is a general rule to apply it in all chanting meditations and during most pranayams. Whenever you are holding the breath in or out, it is usually applied unless instructed otherwise. Sit comfortably with the spine straight. Lift the chest and sternum upward. Gently stretch the back of the neck straight by pulling the chin toward the back of the neck. The head stays level and centered, and does not tilt forward or to either side. The muscles of the neck and throat remain loose. Keep the muscles of the face and brow relaxed.

Japji Sahib: An inspired poem, or scripture composed by Guru Nanak. *Japji Sahib* provides a view of the cosmos, the soul, the mind, the challenge of life, and describes the impact of our actions. Its 40 stanzas are the source of many mantras and can be used as a whole or in part to guide both your mind and your heart.

Japa: Literally "to repeat." It is the conscious, alert, and precise repetition of a mantra.

Ji: Literally meaning "soul," used as a term of endearment or sign of respect.

Kakars (the 5Ks): The five symbols worn by baptized Sikhs: Kesh, Kirpan, Katcheras, Kanga and Kara. Uncut hair, small, single-edged sword, special cotton underwear, wooden comb and steel bracelet, respectively.

Khalsa: Traditionally and literally it means "Pure One." In this path it refers to a pure state of consciousness and lifestyle, that sees the purity in all.

Kriya: Literally means "completed action." An integrated sequence of postures, breath, and sound that work together to manifest a particular state. Kundalini Yoga as taught by Yogi Bhajan® is structured in kriyas, a sequence of postures and yoga techniques used to produce a particular impact on the psyche, body, or self. The structure of each kriya has been designed to generate, organize, and deliver a particular state or change of state, thereby completing a cycle of effect.

Kundalini: Comes from the word "Kundal," curled hair; coiled energy; the creative potential of an individual.

Kundalini Yoga: A Raj Yoga that creates vitality in the body, balance in the mind, and openness to the spirit. It is used by the householder, busy in the world, to create immediate clarity. The fourth Guru in the Sikh tradition, Guru Ram Das, was acknowledged as the greatest Raj Yogi. He opened this long-secret tradition to all.

Langar: Free kitchen associated with Sikh worship service.

Long Deep Breathing: One of the most basic yogic breaths. It uses the full capacity of the lungs. Long Deep Breathing starts by filling the abdomen, then expanding the chest, and finally lifting the upper ribs and clavicle. The exhale is the reverse: first the upper deflates, then the middle, and finally the abdomen pulls in and up, as the Navel Point pulls back toward the spine.

Mantra: Sounds or words that tune or control the mind. Man means mind. Trang is the wave or movement of the mind. Mantra is a wave, a repetition of sound and rhythm that directs or controls the mind. When you recite a mantra you have impact: through the meridian points in the mouth, through its meaning, through its pattern of energy, through its rhythm, and through its naad—energetic shape in time. Recited correctly a mantra will activate areas of the nervous system and brain and allow you to shift your state and the perceptual vision or energetic ability associated with it.

Mudra: Mudra means "seal." It usually refers to hand positions used in meditation and exercise practices. These hand positions are used to seal the body's energy flow in a particular pattern. More generally it can refer to other locks, bandhas and meditation practices that seal the flow of energy.

Mulbandh: This literally means "root lock" and Root Lock is commonly used to refer to mulbandh and is routinely used in Kundalini Yoga. It is a body lock used to balance prana and apana at the Navel Point. This releases reserve energy which is used to arouse the kundalini. It is a contraction of the lower pelvis—the navel point, the sex organs, and the rectum. It coordinates, stimulates, and balances the energies in the lower triangle (first three chakras). This bandh is frequently applied at the end of an exercise or kriya to crystallize its effects. Root Lock is a smooth motion that consists of three parts: First contract the anal sphincter. Feel the muscles lift upward and inward. Once these muscles tighten and move, contract the area around the sex organ. This is experienced as a slight lift and inward rotation of the pubic bone, similar to stopping the flow of urine or Kegel exercises. Then contract the lower abdominal muscles and the Navel Point toward the spine. These three actions are applied together in a smooth, rapid, flowing, motion.

Naad: The inner sound that is subtle and all-present. It is the direct expression of the Absolute. Meditated upon, it pulls the consciousness toward expansion.

Naam: The manifested identity of the essence. The word derives from Naa-ay-ma, which means "that which is not, now is born." A Naam gives identity, form, and expression to that which was only essence. It is also referred to as the Word.

Nadi: Channels or pathways of subtle energy. It is said that there are over 72,000 primary nadis throughout the body.

Navel Point: The sensitive area of the body just below the umbilicus that accumulates and stores life force energy, also known in Eastern martial arts traditions as the *hara*. It is the reserve energy from this area that initiates the flow of the kundalini energy from the base of the spine. If the navel area is strong, your vital force and health are also strong.

Negative Mind: One of the three Functional Minds. It is the fastest and acts to defend you. It asks, "How can this harm me? How can this limit or stop me?" It is also the power to just say no, stop something, or reject a direction of action.

Neutral Mind: The most refined and often the least developed of the three Functional Minds. It judges and assesses. It witnesses and gives you clarity. It holds the power of intuition and the ability to see your purpose and destiny. It is the gateway for awareness.

Nitnem: Literally "repeated every day"; referring to the daily Sikh prayers.

Panj Shabd: Panj means five: *Saa Taa Naa Maa*, that is S, T, N, M, A. It is the "atomic" or naad form of the mantra Sat Nam. It is used to increase intuition, balance the hemispheres of the brain, and to create a destiny for someone when there was none.

Pauri (pauree): Literally "step" or "ladder." Refers to a particular poetic form used in the Siri Guru Granth Sahib.

Pavan Guru: Literally, the "breath of the guru." It is the transformative wisdom that is embedded in the patterns of breath, especially those patterns generated in the expression of naad, in sound or mantra.

Pingala: One of the three major channels (nadis) for subtle energy in the body. It is associated with the flow of breath through the right nostril and represents the qualities of the sun—energy, heat, action, and projective power. It is associated with the functions of the sympathetic nervous system but is not identical to it or derived from it.

Positive Mind: One of the three Functional Minds. It elaborates, magnifies, extends, and assists. It asks, "How can this help me? How can I use this? What is the positive side of this?"

Prabhupati: The third stage of spiritual discipline, when one's own will is aligned to the Will of God.

Prakirti: The creation, the creativity, the matter that has been created by the Creator. Earth is Prakirti.

Prana: The universal life force that gives motion. It is the breath in air. It is the subtle breath of the *purusha* as it vibrates with a psychophysical energy or presence. Prana regulates the modes and moods of the mind.

Pranayam: Regulated breathing patterns or exercises.

Pratyahar: One of the eight limbs of yoga, it is the synchronization of the thoughts with the Infinite. To quote Yogi Bhajan; "Pratyahar is the control of the mind through the withdrawal of the senses. The joy in your life, which you really want to enjoy, is within you. There is nothing more precise than you within you. The day you find the you within you, your mind will be yours. In pratyahar we bring everything to zero (*shuniya*), as pranayam brings everything to Infinity."

Purkha: The Creator

Raj Yog: The Royal Path of Yoga.

Saa Taa Naa Maa: See Panj Shabd

Sadhana: A spiritual discipline; the early morning practice of yoga, meditation, and other spiritual exercises.

Sadhu: A disciplined spiritual person.

Sahasrara: The Crown or 10th Gate; the 1,000-petaled lotus which opens upon the awakening of the kundalini.

Sat: Existence; what is; the subtle essence of Infinity itself; often translated as Truth.

Sat Nam: The essence or seed embodied in form; the identity of truth. When used as a greeting it means "I greet and salute that reality and truth which is your soul." It is called the Bij Mantra—the seed for all that comes.

Segmented Breath: A pranayam that divides the breath into clear segmented parts in specific ratios.

Seva: Selfless service.

Shabd: Sound, especially subtle sound or sound imbued with consciousness. It is a property or emanation of consciousness itself. If you meditate on shabd it awakens your awareness.

Shabd Guru: These are sounds spoken by the Gurus; the vibration of the Infinite Being which transforms your consciousness; the sounds and words captured by the Gurus in the writings which comprise the Siri Guru Granth Sahib.

Shakti: Universal creative energy; one's self-projection; feminine aspect of God; God's power in manifestation; woman. The creative power and principle of existence itself. Without it nothing can manifest or bloom.

Shuniya: A state of the mind and consciousness where the ego is brought to zero or complete stillness. There a power exists. It is the fundamental power of a Kundalini Yoga teacher. When you become shuniya then the One will carry you. You do not grasp or act. With folded hands you "are not." It is then that Nature acts for you.

Shushmana: One of the three major channels (nadis) for subtle energy in the body. It is associated with the central channel of the spine and is the place of neutrality through which the kundalini travels when awakened. When mantra is vibrated from this place it has the power of soul and consciousness.

Siddhis: Occult powers.

Sikh: Sikh means a seeker of truth, and refers to one who follows the Sikh religion.

Sikh Dharma: A living experience of values as taught in the Siri Guru Granth Sahib and exemplified by the 10 Sikh Gurus.

Sikh Gurus: In the Sikh tradition there were 10 living Gurus and one Guru, the Shabd Guru—the Word that guided and flowed through each of them. This succession of 10 Gurus revealed the Sikh path over a 200-year period. They were:

1st Sikh Guru: Guru Nanak	6th Sikh Guru: Guru Hargobind
2nd Sikh Guru: Guru Angad	7th Sikh Guru: Guru Har Rai
3rd Sikh Guru: Guru Amar Das	8th Sikh Guru: Guru Har Krishan
4th Sikh Guru: Guru Ram Das	9th Sikh Guru: Guru Teg Bahadur
5th Sikh Guru: Guru Arjan	10th Sikh Guru: Guru Gobind Singh

The 10th Sikh Guru, Guru Gobind Singh, passed the Guruship to the Siri Guru Granth Sahib, which embodies the writings, teachings, and sound current of the Gurus.

Simran: A deep meditative process in which the naam of the Infinite is remembered and dwelled in without conscious effort.

Siri Guru Granth Sahib: Sacred compilation of the words of the Sikh Gurus as well as of Hindu, Muslim, Sufi, and other saints. It captures the expression of consciousness and truth derived when in a state of divine union with God. It is written in naad and embodies the transformative power and structure of consciousness in its most spiritual and powerful clarity. It is a source of many mantras.

Sitali Pranayam: A cooling breath done through the curled tongue.

Sohang (or Sohung): "I am God, God is me."

Spiritual Name or Destiny Name: A name that describes the spiritual destiny a person should strive for in life.

Sukhmani: Peace Lagoon; a prayer written by Guru Arjan, the Song of Peace.

Tattvas: A category of cosmic existence; a stage of reality or being; a "thatness" of differentiated qualities. In total there are 36 tattvas. Each wave of differentiation has its own rules and structure. The final five tattvas are called the gross elements and have the phasic qualities and relationships of ether, air, fire, water, and earth.

Ten Bodies: We are all spiritual beings having a human experience. In order to have this experience the spirit takes on 10 bodies or vehicles. They are the Soul Body, the three Mental Bodies (Negative, Positive, and Neutral Minds), the Physical Body, Pranic Body, Arcline Body, Auric Body, Subtle Body, and Radiant Body. Each body has its own quality, function, and realm of action.

Third Eye Point: The sixth chakra or center of consciousness. It is located at a point on the forehead between the eyebrows. Associated with the functioning of the pituitary gland, it is the command center and integrates the parts of the personality. It gives you insight, intuition, and the understanding of meanings and impacts beyond the surface of things. For this reason it is the focal point in many meditations.

Uddiyana bandh or Diaphragm Lock: The name of this lock comes from a Sanskrit word which means "to fly up." In this bandh, the energy of the lower abdomen rises. The uddiyana bandh crosses the mind-body barrier, vertically integrating the emotional qualities and allowing circulation of the pranic energy into the central channel, the sushmuna. Diaphragm Lock is only applied on the exhale. Pull the entire abdominal region, especially the area above the Navel Point, upward and back toward the spine.

Trikuti Mantra: A three-part mantra, e.g. Wahe Guru (*Whaa-hay Guroo*)

Wahe Guru: A mantra of ecstasy and dwelling in God. It is the Infinite teacher of the soul. Also called the Gur Mantra.

Wahe Guru Ji ka Khalsa, Wahe Guru Ji ki Fateh: "My purity belongs to God, all victory belongs to God!"

Yantra: A visual representation of a thought, a concept, or energy which captures the *antra (anter)*, or essence of it symbolically.

Yogi: One who has attained a state of yoga (union) where polarities are mastered and transcended. One who practices the disciplines of yoga and has attained self-mastery.